# ARROGANCE
## THE CONQUESTS OF XERXES

COLLEGE LIBRARY
ST. JOSEPH'S COLLEGE

# ARROGANCE
## THE CONQUESTS OF XERXES

*by*

## LOUIS COUPERUS

*Decorations by*

### THEODORE NADEJEN

*Translated by*

### FREDERICK H. MARTENS

COLLEGE LIBRARY ST. JOSEPH'S COLLEGE 1852 Phila., Pa.

PT 5825 .A735 .C856

03931

**MCMXXX**

## FARRAR & RINEHART, INC.

ON MURRAY HILL, NEW YORK

RELEASE

PT5825.A735 ST. JOSEPH'S UNIVERSITY STX
Arrogance;

3 9353 00114 8277

COPYRIGHT, 1930, BY FARRAR & RINEHART, INC.
PRINTED IN THE UNITED STATES OF AMERICA
ALL RIGHTS RESERVED

# CONTENTS

# CONTENTS (*continued*)

# ARROGANCE
## THE CONQUESTS OF XERXES

## CHAPTER I

## ATOSSA'S LITTLE WAR

"PERSIANS! I wish to do no new thing, nor yet aught which might offend the gods. I wish only to achieve world dominion." So Xerxes spoke to his nobles, who were gathered together in the spreading *arpahana* in Susa. And he made a graceful gesture with his sceptre in order to emphasize the fact that in truth he was very modest and honest in his dealings with gods and men.

Xerxes, the King of Kings, was seated upon a lofty throne. It was supported by two golden lions with savagely distorted faces, and along each side of the broad steps leading up to it were ranged six

[3]

other golden lions with faces savagely distorted. Xerxes himself was in the bloom of young manhood, and his winning smile and winning glance—as though he felt obliged to make clear to everyone that the achievement of world dominion was a goal to which the King of Kings, the King of the Persians, might well aspire—radiated from his face out into the hall and over all his nobles, like sunlight. And from wherever they might be standing, his nobles crowded forward, from the farthest reaches, in the middle and in the far rear of the hall, between rows of columns that faded into the distance. Many of the lesser lords, standing afar off, did not hear Xerxes. This made little difference. They agreed at all times with the more influential nobles, who could hear without difficulty what the Basileus was saying in his well-modulated voice.

It was late autumn and the sun—the priests falsely declared it to be the eye of Ormuzd—cast his rays obliquely into the throne-room, in a glittering, dust-moted powder along slanting roads of radiance, through the square, deep-set window openings.

In the interior of the hall were densely ranged slender columns, columns which first of all terminated in calyxed capitals and then, above these, blossomed out in two double scrolls of blue-grey marble. These volutes were weighed with the kneeling torsos of bulls, also of blue-grey marble, well-nigh too lofty in proportion to the slenderness of the columns, and these kneeling blue-grey bulls supported the enormous, gilded beams of the cedarwood roof.

Beneath it swam vapoury azure shadows. The sunlight floated behind and around the princes and the king, and those of simple mind might easily believe that divine spirits descended from the heavens

[4]

along this sun-dust path and hovered about Xerxes. Or, that he himself, his speech concluded, would ascend on them to the skies, there to meet Ormuzd, his master, and this quite as legitimately as he might achieve world empire. Xerxes was tall. And seated there on his throne supported by lions showing their fangs, with his captivating smile and clad in his golden mantle woven by the hands of Persian queens, he impressed even those grandees who stood farthest removed from him. The symmetrical curls which fell from beneath his tiara over his amber-hued countenance, the symmetrical curls of his beard, were blue-black, black with a blue reflection. Amiably Xerxes continued:

"We have already conquered Egypt. Egypt belongs to us."

He spoke no more than the truth, and his nobles were aware of it. He had recently conquered Egypt. Egypt had been made a tributary of Persia, and Xerxes' armies had returned home during the months just past.

"Since Cyrus deprived Astyages of his crown and seized the Median kingdom, we have never folded our hands in idleness, neither I nor my ancestors."

Xerxes glanced about him with a smile; a low murmur of approval, like the hum of many bees, buzzed through the throne-room.

"May God guide us!" said Xerxes solemnly, and added in explanation:

"The God of the Persians!"

For every nation has its God, and even its gods.

But Xerxes wished to point out emphatically that the God of the Persians had led his people in their striving for that world empire which was now almost within his grasp.

[5]

The King of Kings went fluently on:

"You yourselves know that Cyrus, that Cambyses, that my never-to-be-forgotten memorable father Darius added countless provinces to our empire. I can do no less than they, and must follow the tradition of my dynasty. I must conquer a kingdom, a kingdom that is not inferior to those already overcome. At the same time, I wish to avenge us on Persia's enemies. You cannot fail to grasp my meaning. Crossing a bridge which I shall fling over the Hellespont, I mean to invade Greece with my armies. The Athenians, in particular, have insulted my never-to-be-forgotten father, as well as all Persia. Hence I wish to conquer Athens. Besides, the Athenians cast the first stone. Together with Aristagoras the Milesian—one of our slaves, for Miletus belongs to us—they came to Sardis and there desecrated the sacred groves. They are barbarians, though that is what they call us. When Datis and Ataphrenes invaded Greece with our armies . . . Well, the less said about Marathon the better. Yet the historic truth with regard to Marathon is still far from being generally known.

"To return to my point of departure: the more I consider the conquest of Greece, the more I am taken with the following simple plan. Pelops settled the Peloponnesus. But Pelops was really a Persian slave. For he was a Phrygian, and Phrygia belongs to us.

"As a matter of fact, the whole world belongs to us. I wish Persia to have no other boundaries than the skies, and that the sun shall never set in my empire. Incidentally, the Magians have prophesied that a world empire will some day arise on which the sun will never set. Of course, that means Persia. So I wish to conquer all Europe, and become King of

Kings throughout the world. Once the Greeks have been defeated, no other city or people will offer further resistance. All nations, whether guilty or no, will bow beneath our yoke.

"So I will be greatly indebted to you, all you satraps, if you do as I tell you. Levy men in all your satrapies! He who can show me the finest body of soldiers shall receive a gift of rare beauty from my royal hand. Thus I decree. Yet, since I would not have it seem that I decide everything according to my own opinion, I beg that you, my nobles, will discuss this matter and not withhold your much-valued counsel from me."

Xerxes looked amiably about him, proud of his skill and his concluding words. He knew how to handle his nobles. He knew positively that his satraps, when he stooped to them with such amiability and begged for their advice, would advise only in accordance with his will. And looking about him with his confident smile, powdered from head to foot with the golden dust of the descending sun-path as though he had but just come down from the skies, Xerxes was well aware that the nobles standing at the back of the tremendous throne-room were stretching their necks and cupping their ears in their hands to catch the king's last word, which already had died away. Yet he was not disturbed because they had understood nothing. Why were they not great, instead of petty nobles? Why did they stand so far removed from his throne and from his glory, shoved aside by the greatest grandees? Almost imperceptibly Xerxes shrugged his shoulders, enwrapped in the golden mantle and irradiant in the sunlight.

Beside him Mardonius had risen from his seat that

rested upon lions' claws. He was Xerxes' brother-in-law. Like many Persians he bore a name that sounded Greek. For Persian as Xerxes sounded and sounds, so Mardonius sounded and sounds purely Greek.

Mardonius was an enthusiastic young general, the husband of Xerxes' sister, Artozostra. He had already fought against the Greeks. He had been in Macedonia with his countless host, but his fleet had been totally destroyed by a storm off Mount Athos: three hundred ships, over twenty thousand men. Sea monsters had devoured the drowning crews. Mardonius had never been able to forget that neither his enthusiasm nor yet his army had fully triumphed over the Greeks, over the tempest's power, the malice of circumstance and Fate. So in a measure, at the drinking bouts, he had influenced his brother-in-law to speak the words the King of Kings had that moment pronounced. Yet Mardonius, whose enthusiasm kept him preoccupied, and who was a general rather than a statesman, was glad to give his brother-in-law all the credit of spurring on the Persian nobles to a new war against Greece. He exclaimed with enthusiasm: "Exalted Despot! You are not alone the greatest Persian upon whom the sun has hitherto shone, but the greatest of all upon whom it may shine in the future."

Mardonius was entirely sincere in his enthusiasm. He intended no irony; he did not know what irony was. His was the soul of a warrior and of an ecstatic dreamer. All in all, his was a lofty soul. But he was unaware of this, he beheld only the grandeur of Persia and of its king. And so he cried enthusiastically:

"No! You will not suffer the Ionians of Europe,

this low, contemptible people, longer to insult us! Have we not defeated the Sacæ, the Indians, Ethiopians, Assyrians and numberless other peoples, who never did us any harm? Shall we not now make up our minds to defeat these Greeks who went to Sardis to desecrate our holy fanes, who dared to set our sacred groves afire? What have we to fear? The number of their soldiers? Their wealth? We have greater armies and more notable treasures. Besides, they are always foolish enough to insist on fighting in the open plains. So they may destroy our more numerous armies in the open plains—provided they have the courage! For they lacked courage to do battle with me in Macedonia, when I was commanding the Persian armies there. O King, in battle we are not alone the most courageous, but the most experienced! Victory will be ours."

The murmur of approval vibrated in the great throne-room like the humming of many bees. Yet this murmur was audible only because it was customary, at the Persian court, to approve of a speaker's words as a matter of caution. At bottom the Persians—for they recalled Marathon—did not want this war, although Xerxes had declared that the historic truth regarding Marathon was far from known. Therefore they were much pleased when from a second seat, resting on golden lions' claws, there arose old Artabanus, the son of Hystaspes and Xerxes' uncle on his father's side. The uncle said:

"Basileus! If you would prove gold, match your gold with other gold! Take your impressions and those of Mardonius, and weigh them in the balance against mine. Did I not, in the past, advise your father, my brother Darius, not suddenly to make war on the Scythians? He did not take my advice, and lost his armies in Scythia. You wish to build a bridge across the Hellespont, in order to lead your armies to Europe. Suppose our enemies destroy our fleet and our bridge across the Hellespont? How then will you lead your armies home again?

"Great King, beware! Those in high places are most exposed to danger. The lightning strikes towers and elephants, yet ants swarm about in hiding while the storm is at its worst.

"But you, Mardonius, cease reviling the Greeks! They have never deserved your scorn. Rather should you recall all that you now forget or that you explain after your own fashion! Then you will not run the risk of evoking a catastrophe that will overwhelm the Persians. Nor will you find yourself vanquished, and stretched out on Attic or Lacedæmonian soil, a prey for dogs and vultures."

These words of a wisdom approved by years pleased neither Xerxes nor Mardonius. Yet the grandees' murmur of applause hummed through the hall, as ever after counsel or speech. After all, one never could foretell what the king would decide to do. In any case, it was a wise precaution to hum politely. Xerxes rose in wrath and cried out to his uncle:

"You are a coward and an old woman! I shall leave you here with the other women. I am the son of Darius, and I count Hystaspes, Arsames, Cyrus, Cambyses and Achæmenes among my ancestors. I will be no lesser man than they. Nor do I strive for more nor less than world empire. I want war. I have decided upon war."

The nobles listened to Xerxes with terror. Nevertheless, the commendatory bees' hum again buzzed along their beards through the throne-room. Artabanus had sat down again upon his stool with head gloomily bowed. Only Mardonius gazed around joyously, like a young lion, and Xerxes turned his golden back on the assembled nobles to indicate that the council was over.

He did not stride through the obliquely falling sun-rays to the palace of Ormuzd, but withdrew to his apartments, content because his nobles had decided upon war with Greece yet—because of Artabanus—not entirely satisfied.

The throng of princes, satraps and grandees streamed out of the throne-room. And in that hall which was now emptying, whose hundred columns supported the cedar beams of the roof on their double bull-torsos, one could more distinctly see the abandoned throne, with its roaring lions glittering and irradiant with light.

The same lions, the lions which followed each other in sequential movement, the royal lions, symbols of supreme might and power, now were increasingly visible on the glazed tile frieze surrounding the immeasurable throne-room: the ivory-white lions with their green and blue manes, and their monstrous, heavy-muscled shoulder blades, the lions with gilded yawning maws and high-stretched tails.

When the hall was quite empty, Atossa, the mother of Xerxes, an old woman who squinted because of her near-sightedness, and who was completely shrouded in a violet mantle, appeared from behind a gilded lattice. To the three other royal widows of Darius who clustered about her, the All-highest, she said:

"Now I am sure of my little war. I want some Athenian and Dorian slaves. There are none better."

## CHAPTER II

## XERXES' DREAM

NO SOONER was Xerxes entirely alone, than solitude, night and silence lent to thing a different aspect than they had worn while he occupied his high seat in the throne-room his smiling eyes resting on his satraps. He frowned He seated himself on the edge of his couch, a thron raised upon golden lion-claws, but now a throne o slumber, and cupped his bearded chin in the palm o his hand. He reflected, and suddenly discovered world of difficulties.

Declare war against the Greeks? Fling a bridg across the Hellespont? There were the ceasele

[12]

storms which raged about Mount Athos, and already had blown away one of his fleets! Foaming with rage he shook his fist at the god of the wind, who would not favour him. He suddenly decided not to undertake a war against the Greeks, and his decision was very human in its accord with the abrupt changeability of his resolves. In his night clothes and in the quiet of his bed-chamber a King of Kings often reaches a decision quite opposed to that made in his golden mantle of maintenance, amid the pomp of his royal state. Xerxes, nevertheless, was dissatisfied with himself and with everyone else, with his mother and with Mardonius. He flung himself violently down to rest, turned his back to the room and fell asleep. (In those days he did not yet suffer from insomnia.)

And while he slept he dreamed. Dreams are divinities—petty divinities, yet divinities none the less—and they may be good or evil. As a rule Zeus—whom the Persians adore as well as the Greeks, yet in another manner—sends out the good dreams to gods, heroes and men. Was Xerxes' dream sent him by Zeus or by Ahriman? History has not recorded. We only learn that the dream approached Xerxes in the shape of a tall, radiant, winged warrior, who said to the king:

"How, Xerxes? Do you now of a sudden wish no war, after having had your satraps call in the recruits for three years? Whence comes this lack of spirit? I tell you, you must decide on war."

Angry and terrified, Xerxes awoke. War? No, he wanted no war. He cursed his silly dream, again turned his back on the room and fell asleep. The next day he once more gathered his satraps about him. Many of them had already started for their satrapies because of the levies; but, overtaken by speeding couriers and informed of the king's command, thy turned back with their wagons and horses and suites. They entered the throne-room at the very moment when Xerxes was explaining that he had changed his mind. In a speech full of generalizations, he was discussing the caution he in future intended to observe.

He spoke well and acceptably, and he enjoyed hearing himself talk about caution. The satraps who had just that moment returned did not at once grasp his meaning, nor did they understand . . . because they stood too far away. They cupped their ears in their hands and thus tried to catch Xerxes' extremely graceful sentences concerning caution. Then they heard Xerxes offer an apology. For the sake of rhetorical effect he did so in a somewhat tearful voice. He offered his excuses to his uncle Artabanus because he had called him an old woman the day before. It had not been said in earnest, declared Xerxes, and expatiated on the various shades of meaning attached to the expression "old woman" in Persian. Uncle Artabanus was touched. His eyes grew moist. From the place where he sat he made an imploring gesture toward his royal nephew. He should not continue in that strain, he really should not. Xerxes closed with oratorical fervour, which made a deep impression.

"Therefore I desire no war with the Greeks. Let all of you return to your homes and remain quiet, gentlemen!" Then he turned his back on them, while they fell to earth on their faces, in joy and reverence.

## CHAPTER III

## THE MAGIANS' PRAYER

**M**ARDONIUS, however, was not pleased. He was obstinate, and he felt the urge to act. The court at Susa bored him, and he was passionately in favour of a war with Greece. It also happened to be one of Atossa's ideas—a little war with Greece to secure some Attic and Dorian slave girls. So Mardonius excused himself on the score of a headache and did not appear at the gala banquet that night. He quarrelled about it with his wife Artozostra. He even went so far as to tell her, Xerxes' sister, that her name was anything but euphonius. Artozostra! With intention he pro-

[15]

nounced the name with a scornful inflection.  She objected and made no bones about informing him that his own name was far too Greek for a Persian. Mardonius!  She cast his Greek name in his face. He became much exercised and insisted that other princes of the blood had Grecized names.  He wept with rage.  And when she saw him weep she wept with him and took him in her arms.  He embraced her and gave her permission to go to the gala banquet alone.  On this occasion Xerxes, with his wife Amestris, was installed on a banquet throne, and was much surprised when Artozostra excused her husband Mardonius.  He had a headache, she said. Xerxes was not convinced.

That night as Xerxes slept, his dream once more drew near.

"Son of Darius," spoke the dream.  "Give ear to what will take place if you do not follow my advice and go forth and do battle with the Greeks! You will shrivel up and become small, so very small."

And Xerxes saw the dream, with an ironic gesture, point out into what a wretchedly small Xerxes he would shrivel, one raised no more than a few inches above the ground.

Xerxes awoke in a fright.  The sweat poured from his brow.

"Uncle!" he cried.  "Uncle Artabanus!"

From one adjoining chamber Queen Amestris, from another Atossa, rushed in.

"I want uncle!" shouted Xerxes petulantly, in a raised voice.

From other palace chambers, amid guards and chambermaids, Artozostra and Mardonius hurried up.

"I want Uncle Artabanus!" cried Xerxes.

He flung himself into his uncle's arms and Artabanus led him to his own room.

"Uncle," exclaimed Xerxes. "The dream has visited me for the second time. The dream prophesied that I would dwindle to this size"—and with his hand Xerxes measured off his future diminished state from the floor—"if I do not declare war against Greece."

Uncle Artabanus was violently alarmed. Such a diminution, when one dreamed it, was a symbol, a symbol of the downfall of the Persian empire. What to do?

"Uncle," whispered Xerxes, as he shuddered and pressed his blue-black beard against his uncle's grey one. "Listen! Yet let us whisper lest the dream be eavesdropping. We must seek to discover the dream's meaning and put it to the test. I must know who sent me the dream, whether Zeus or Ormuzd or Ahriman. Tomorrow night, therefore, you must wrap yourself in my mantle of state, and then in my nightrobe, and lie down to sleep in my bed. If the dream appears to you and gives you the identical command it laid on me, then the dream is sent by the gods. And in such case I will know what I must do."

Uncle Artabanus begged to be excused. He was, so he said, unworthy to wear his royal nephew's robes and to lie on a king's couch. But Xerxes was magnanimously insistent. His uncle agreed in a whisper, for it would not do to rouse the dream's suspicions.

The following evening Xerxes and Uncle Artabanus mysteriously stole away on tiptoe, since the latter was to don the king's mantle of state. Then Xerxes left his uncle. And the uncle made his way to Xerxes' bed-chamber and there disrobed, as though he were the king himself. And he lay down to sleep as though he were the king.

While he slept the dream actually visited him. Yet the dream was quite well aware that the sleeper was not Xerxes.

"Artabanus!" cried the dream. "Why did you withhold Xerxes from declaring war on Greece?"

Much frightened, Artabanus hurried to Xerxes and, while they exchanged nightrobes, said:

"O royal nephew! The dream has been sent by the great gods. That is past all doubt. I advised you not to go to war because I remembered Cyrus vanquished by the Massagetæ, and Cambyses vanquished by the Ethiopians, and your never-to-be-forgotten father Darius vanquished by the Scythians. So it seemed best to me to keep quiet and not to challenge Fate, after all. Order your satraps to call in all the recruits for the next few years and march out to battle!"

"The God of the Persians will go with us," cried Xerxes.

That night he dreamed another dream. The following morning when he saw the Magians, who very exactly one after the other—there were three times nine of them—paced through the long columned portico of the palace on the way to their hall of assembly, he noticed that they were out of sorts. He knew why. The Magi were out of sorts because the King of Kings had not asked them to interpret his first and second dreams, and the dream of Artabanus. They moved on and acted as though they had not seen the king.

But Xerxes called out amiably:

"O ye Magians!"

[18]

They all turned around at the identical moment. Their pointed mitres stood starkly erect, like horns. Their blue-black beards curled symmetrically. They all seemed alike old, alike venerable, alike tall, alike wise. They all resembled each other in their awe-inspiring appearance.

"O ye Magians!" said Xerxes, smiling. "Tell me the meaning of the dream I dreamed last night!"

He told them his dream. An olive wreath had wound itself about his brow and had then put forth branches that covered all the world. Thereupon the wreath had disappeared.

The Magians—three times nine in number—without even consulting each other with a glance, all cried out at the same time:

"World dominion!"

Xerxes started at the sound of their voices. It seemed as though their seven and twenty voices were one single voice.

And as Xerxes, still frightened, remained where he was, the Magians turned away their heads, covered with the pointed mitres, and moved forward in the direction of their assembly hall. The hall of the Magians was completely enclosed in the mass of the palace buildings, and because it was dark no one of the Magians observed that about the curled beard of each of their number there played a wry grin. In silence they entered their hall and smiled.

The hall was as broad as the night, a dark night, and in it was neither image nor altar. For the Persians dedicated neither altars nor idols to their gods, nor even temples accessible to the people. No sooner had the Magians entered their own shrine, as broad and dark as night, than as though by a miracle it became bright with a mysterious radiance.

[19]

Then the Magians each saw the others' grins.

They were violently alarmed, and flung themselves on the ground before the great round eye of Ormuzd, which shone at the end of the hall.

With one voice they cried:

"Have mercy on Persia, O God!"

## CHAPTER IV

## MOUNT ATHOS

THE Persians reproached the Greeks with being "Barbarians," and the Greeks returned the compliment. In fact, the Greeks called everyone who was not a Greek a "Barbarian," and did so emphatically. Perhaps both were right, perhaps neither was. In any event, the Greeks were a young, vigorous people, waxing in growth, while the Persians, after three generations, had already attained super-refinement. Probably it was because of this that they could not understand each other. A Greek was huffed by a Persian's dress, behaviour, faith and customs. And these same things the Persian found objectionable in the Greek. Friendship between them was out of the question.

In addition, Xerxes despised the Greeks. And the Magians also despised the Greeks; they considered them an inferior people because they built temples to their gods containing images of the gods accessible to the common herd. True, the Magians also sacrificed to Zeus, yet they did so on the loftiest mountain heights, amid thunder and lightnings, and they made burnt offerings to sun, moon, earth, fire, water and wind. Yet Persia's favourite god was Mithra. He was at one and the same time man and woman, god and goddess, power inceptive and power receptive, comprehensible to all mankind.

Since Cyrus had conquered all Asia—and that was little more than half a century past—the Persians ruled over a great number of peoples. Under Cyrus the country had been young and vigorous, as Greece now was. Yet as soon as the Persian kings began to rule such a multitude of nations, the super-refinement of Persia began. Such is the law of bloom, growth and decay. Xerxes did not see things in this light; he did not even suspect that he was super-refined. He hated the Greeks and had resolved on war in accordance with his dreams.

He devoted four years to preparation. Throughout his whole gigantic empire levies were made among all the peoples subject to him, and supplies were everywhere collected.

Two difficulties, in particular, preoccupied the Great King: the Hellespont and Mount Athos. Xerxes, who had already decided to fling a bridge of boats across the Hellespont, now commanded that Mount Athos be cut through, so that his fleet might have a safe passageway into Greek waters. Then

[22]

there would be no danger of his ships again being blown away and destroyed in the neighbourhood of the cape by the irreconcilable Greek gods of the wind. In all the squares and streets of the Persian cities, especially in Susa and in Sardis, during the first months of warlike preparation, the Persians crowded about gigantic posters, on which, in delicate script, appeared the king's letter addressed to Mount Athos:

"Divine Athos, you who stretch your summit up into the clouds, dare no longer to challenge me, the King of Kings! Place no all-too-recalcitrant blocks of stone in the way of my builders and slaves! Or else I will have you carried away piecemeal and cast into the sea as refuse!"

The letter itself was carried to the mountain by the royal mail, and graven on one of Athos' rocky walls, so that the mountain could never claim that it had not received Xerxes' missive.

From the port of Eleus in the Thracian Chersonese whole squadrons put out, triremes after triremes, to cut through Mount Athos. This mountain formed an enormous, venerated and far-flung cape, projecting majestically into the sea like some ship of the Titans, turned to rock. Opposite the mountain lie towns and villages, half-buried in gorges and valleys. A peninsula from twenty to thirty stadia in breadth connects the cape with the mainland. This peninsula is a valley, and in this valley lies the town of Sana.

Tens of thousands of soldier recruits arrived in Sana and flooded the small, peaceful Greek city. Bubares and Artachæus were their generals. These tens of thousands of soldier recruits were drilled with the lash. So Persian discipline decreed. Artachæus, the Achæmenian, was a giant in stature, which is

[23]

invariably impressive in the case of a general. The Persians always admired bodily size and all that was colossal. Artachæus was five royal cubits less four fingers in height, which comes to seven feet plus some inches. His voice was terrifying. When he raised it, his officers, the mechanics, and even the sergeants, who bellowed as they plied the soldiers' backs with the lash, were frightened.

Under the drilling and cursing good progress was made with the work in hand. To each of the united Persian peoples was assigned the task of boring through a bit of Athos. All was well divided. Every nation measured off its portion with ropes and steel cables. Work was begun near the city of Sana, and while the lashes cracked, the men of the engineer detachments of the Persian army swung pickaxe, bored and dug. Mount Athos split asunder very slowly, but split it did. From one to the other sea the mountain was riven as a punishment, because some years before the Greek gods of the wind, who swirled about its summit, had blown away Mardonius' fleet.

The sea monsters which in that past time had swallowed the drowning seamen, now rose up out of the raging waves to see what was going on. Furtively, and greatly astonished, they peered at the cleavage, apprehensive lest, if Athos really were cut in two, they could count on no Persian victims in the future. Every morning, as a precaution—even now that the work was progressing favourably—the Persians offered sacrifices to the evil winds and to the sea monsters.

The cut was increasing in depth. The water was already beginning to gush up about the feet of the stone-breakers who were digging deepest and standing lowest. These diggers and hewers dragged the masses of rock up to those standing on ladders above them. From lower to ever higher ladders, fastened to the rock by iron clamps, the blocks of stone rose in the hands of the men passing them to each other— the tens of thousands—and the lashes whistled. The tortured rock groaned and moaned. Picks and sledgehammers raged with a wild music of iron on stone between the already receding walls of the cut. Baskets filled with rubble and sand ascended endlessly on the windlass. High up over the peak of the mountain the blocks of rock, the baskets of sand and of rubble swayed to the right and to the left. The lions who had their dens in the caves—at that time there were still lions in Europe—fled or leaped into the sea in their perplexity. The sea monsters devoured them. Athos was splitting, and couriers reported the splitting of Athos to Xerxes, who was making ready to pass from Susa to Sardis. And he sent necklets and armlets, which represented the honorific distinctions of the Persians, to Artachæus and Bubares.

Meanwhile, now and again the embankments of the open trench would crumble when beneath the crack of the whip the picks and hammers had hewed and hammered overmuch. The boulders would plunge thunderingly into the depth upon high-towering ladders and sweating slaves. Then there would be cursings and floggings, a general clearing up, and the rock would again rise on newly-erected ladders. Artachæus, the giant, rode his huge charger high up over the rocky mountain crests to superintend the work. His abnormally powerful arms were ringed with the many armlets the king had sent him.

Vultures soared above the toilers in the upper air, coveting the corpses buried beneath the ruins and now handed up from ladder to ladder, together with the rocks that had caved in, only to be cast down the mountainside with the sand and rubble. At night, when the moon glided through the clouds, and peace lay upon the hills, the vultures circled above the bodies of the dead like winged larvæ, and disposed of them after the Persian fashion. The next day there was hardly a trace of the carrion-stench to be noticed. The Phœnicians, skilful in all ways, proved their skill in this task as well. They excavated their section to a greater breadth than necessary, and narrowed their cut as it grew deeper, so that they avoided all landslides.

Bubares, the general in command of part of these engineers, was a sarcastic soul. When he saw the rank and file toiling and slaving under the lashes of the sergeants—he himself sitting his horse beside the gigantic figure of Artachæus, also in the saddle—he smiled, shrugged his shoulders and leaning over to Artachæus, whispered:

"A piece of insanity! The ships of our fleet could easily enough be carried across the isthmus by their crews. Then the canal would not be needed."

But Artachæus frowned in a dark and awe-inspiring manner and said:

"A canal is better, and this canal will be so broad that two triremes can pass through it abreast."

"Yes, a canal is probably better," Bubares at once agreed.

When it was merely a matter of words Bubares always yielded to Artachæus. Only his smile grew more malicious. But Artachæus did not notice the

malicious smile, and moved his powerful arms so
that his many armlets rattled noisily. Bubares
shoved his own somewhat higher, so that they
would not rattle, and estimated that once the canal
was cut, he'd be rich enough to . . .

CHAPTER V

## THE RICHEST MAN IN ASIA

MEANWHILE Xerxes was on his way to Sardis with a few Cappadocian armies. Who was the satrap who had received from the royal hand the handsomest gift for exhibiting the finest body of troops? History has not recorded his name, and presumably felt no need to do so. Xerxes arrived in Celænæ in Phrygia. His army lay outside the walls. Xerxes inspected the notable sights of the town. In the public square he bent over the broad marble basin in which rises the Catarractes, the river which empties into famed Mæander. When he had seen the spring—which did not strike him as

[28]

remarkable, though it seemed strange that a river should rise in a market-place—he was led into the temple of Apollo. In it was treasured the wine skin fashioned from the epidermis of that flayed Marsyas the Silent who had dared measure himself with Apollo in playing the flute and singing. Apollo was unjust when he had him skinned alive. For Marsyas, the son of Hyagnis who had invented the flute in Celænæ, played his father's instrument better than the god, who doubtless always regarded the flute as inferior to his lyre. Xerxes found the wine skin no more interesting that the source of the Catarractes, and said:

"A second-rate little town, this Celænæ."

Out of humour, he looked about him. It was in the middle of the day and time hung heavy on his hands. The palace he had occupied was an old, decayed structure, which Persian architects and decorators had with difficulty made habitable for a few days. It had been chosen because of its size, and because the king's retinue must be accommodated. Xerxes was about to ask his officers whether there was really nothing else worth seeing in this nest, when a procession approached across the square: camels, asses and a sedan chair.

"Who may this be?" Xerxes asked in surprise.

The bystanders respectfully whispered the information to the king's officers. And they said to Xerxes:

"Great Despot! It is Pythius, the Lydian. After you he is the richest man in the world, and he gave Darius, your father, the golden plane-tree and the golden grapevine that stand in your palace in Susa."

Xerxes was full of expectation. Pythius had left his chair and, surrounded by a numerous suite,

[29]

approached the King of Kings; he nosed the ground, hands and arms outstretched before him, and all the others cast themselves on the earth of Celænæ before Xerxes, hands and arms outstretched before them.

Then Xerxes, after a few polite phrases had been exchanged, asked Pythius how rich he really was. This, as history reports it, sounds like an impertinence. The standard of good manners, even for a king, was different in that day, and Xerxes' question expressed no more than an amiable interest.

So Pythius took it. And the question pleased him because it led up quite naturally to his own objective. He said:

"King of Kings! Why should I conceal it, and declare that I have never counted my wealth? I will tell you what wealth I possess. I have just made the count. No sooner did I know you would visit the Grecian Sea than I counted my treasure, in order to give it all to you as tribute for the war. And I counted two thousand talents of silver and four million less seven thousand of those golden staters which we call darics, after the image of Darius which they bear. I offer this treasure to you for the war chest, Great Despot."

Xerxes was content and felt much flattered.

"Yet you yourself? How will you manage to exist, Pythius?"

"Lord," said the Lydian modestly, "I have my estates, cultivated by my slaves."

He said nothing of the eight thousand talents of silver and the twenty millions in golden staters which he, together with his sons, has buried under the mosaic floors of his palaces and country villas.

Xerxes smiled amiably. He was in a good humour and full of condescension.

"Since my departure from Persia," said he, while a radiant smile played about his blue-black beard, "I have not yet met such noble generosity and exalted patriotism on my way. Receive in exchange, Pythius, my royal thanks and my friendship!"

Xerxes spread his arms, embraced Pythius, and kissed his mouth. This was the highest honour one Persian could show another. A blue-black and a grey beard mingled hairs a moment with affectionate tenderness.

"And," Xerxes added, gently magnanimous, "so that not a single daric of the four million you meant to give me, but do not possess, be missing, I myself, Pythius, will add the lacking seven thousand to them with my royal hand."

A murmur of applause ran through beards and over smooth-shaven lips.

"Enjoy your other possessions undisturbed, Pythius," Xerxes affably continued, "and see to it that in the future you ever act as you have acted but now. You shall not regret it, neither today nor in the days to come. Will you lie as a guest at my royal table?"

Pythius gratefully said he would. He made no allusion to the fact that he himself had provided the royal banquet to which Xerxes had invited him, and that he had entertained the army outside the walls of the town. At the king's side he entered the hastily decorated palace, and did not think it needful to mention that he himself had placed the precious rugs, the golden couches and the missing golden vessels for the table service at the disposal of the royal majordomo.

The day ran its course most agreeably, and the night even more so.

[31]

## CHAPTER VI

## WIVES AND CONCUBINES

MEANWHILE the royal wives had remained behind in Susa. In the royal palace, which at the same time was an enormous citadel, yet comprised a whole swarm of courtyards, porticoes, garden pleasances, halls and terraces, the royal wives, together with many concubines, had stayed when Xerxes went. There were very many of them. About Queen Amestris, about the four royal widows of Darius, Xerxes' never-to-be-forgotten father, about the younger princesses, the concubines and slaves might be counted by the thousands. The

Chief Eunuch knew the exact number, which history has failed to register.

It was spring, and from the garden, mingled with the sweet, cloying odour of cooking preserves, came the fragrance of roses, of Persian roses, great fiery red roses, tens of thousands of them, through the porticoes and into the huge, open, many-columned hall occupied by Queen Amestris, the four royal widows and the princesses.

They were all squatting in a circle on square couches. Queen Amestris, together with her slaves, was weaving at a loom which suspended before her the glittering threads of a mantle she was making for Xerxes. Opposite the queen sat the oldest of the royal widows, Atossa. An almost awe-inspiring reverence was paid her—at least while she spied about the women's room from beneath her drooping eyelids. She was sixty years of age, and a Persian royal widow of sixty is old.

Atossa was the daughter of Cyrus. This in itself gave her the highest claim to reverence. Atossa's life went back to the beginning of the Persian empire's rise. And that not only humanly, but historically as well, commanded reverence. Atossa had been the wife of three Persian kings. All that had happened for more than half a century in the palace at Susa had been part of her life experience. This commanded not only reverence; it was awe-inspiring. She knew every intrigue, every murder, every last secret. Crouching on her couch opposite the weaving Queen Amestris, her aged hands, adorned with heavy amethyst rings, resting idly in her lap, her oriental eyes half-closed under the fringe of her violet veil, she seemed on the watch for still further palace

[33]

mysteries and feared she might miss the very latest one.

Her first husband had been her brother Cambyses. She had married him because the law of the royal clan ordained that the king must raise up his sister to sit beside him as queen. When Cambyses had perished, she had followed the prescribed custom, that the victorious monarch must wed all his predecessor's wives. So she had married pseudo-Smerdis. Those had been times rich in excitement and new happenings for all the palace women, the times of pseudo-Smerdis, the Mede, who claimed he was Smerdis the brother of Cambyses, that Smerdis whom Cambyses had had murdered. When Darius and the other conspirators had unmasked pseudo-Smerdis, Atossa had become the wife of the latest victor, the wife of Darius. Now she was the queen-mother, the mother of Xerxes, King of Kings. She spied about her, in the circle of the royal women, lest some secret, some incipient intrigue might escape her now that she was growing old.

Behind the weaving queen—everywhere there floated an endless murmur of feminine voices—one slave-girl whispered to another, as both busied themselves winding the queen's golden thread on a spool:

"A prophecy declares that Atossa . . ."

"What?" asked the other.

"Will be devoured by the king."

"Brr!" The second slave-girl shuddered; then both giggled.

Yet Atossa had heard her name whispered.

"What did that witch there say?" she cried in a shrill, angry tone.

"Who, Daughter of Cyrus, Mother of Xerxes,

Allhighest Mother?" asked Amestris, peering out from the side of her loom at the venerable Atossa.

"The Sidonian wench behind you. What are the two giggling about?"

"Nothing, Allhighest," said Amestris soothingly, as she went on weaving. "They are children. They laugh when a fly tickles their nose."

"Come here, both of you!" commanded Atossa.

At the same time she seized a whip which lay by her knees on the couch, a whip with an amethyst handle. The Sidonian girl and her companion began to howl, but Atossa gruffly ordered:

"Quick! Make haste!"

The two slave-girls crawled across the vacant middle of the chamber to Atossa's couch.

"Disgusting little sloths!" scolded Atossa, raised her whip and brought it down.

Her trembling old hand was not sure of its aim. Either she missed them or hit them but lightly. The two slave-girls, however, wailed loudly and fled, one to the right, the other to the left, with rhythmic grace as though dancing, to take refuge behind the queen's back.

"Wind up the purple silk!" Amestris bade them, discontentedly. And the girls once more began winding and giggling, while they kept out of sight behind Amestris and her loom. At Atossa's left Artystone crouched on her couch; at her right, on two other couches, crouched Phaidyme and Parmys. They were the other three royal widows, the wives of Darius, Xerxes' never-to-be-forgotten father. There they sat, and about them their slaves were busy.

A crowd of laundresses at this moment dragged in a number of baskets, in which lay the queen's and the

[35]

princesses' veils and handkerchiefs. Beside Parmys sat Artaynte, the youthful, lovely daughter of the king's half-brother Masistes, and beside Artystone sat Artozostra, Xerxes' sister—though not one of Atossa's daughters—the wife of Mardonius, Xerxes' nephew.

The women who had brought in the laundry were not exactly informed with regard to the family relationships existing between the queens and princesses, and the king, his brothers and his nephews. These were complicated and hard to remember. At the Persian court brothers married sisters, nephews and nieces, and all their children married among each other, so that, with the exception of those directly concerned, no one could make head or tail of these relationships. Among the Persians at large no one bothered to do so, nor would the writer of these annals advise anyone else to take the trouble.

The laundress-slaves carried a large basket to Atossa's couch. Atossa squinted into the basket. Her own slave-girls carefully drew out the smoothed and folded veils, while Atossa herself read the laundry list: "Seven violet veils of Egyptian byssus, with gold-embroidered hems."

"Here they are, Allhighest," said Baktra—she was the slave highest in authority—as she exhibited the veils.

"Thrice seven . . ." Atossa continued.

To the other royal wives and to the queen, the slave-girls also brought baskets which they placed before them, and picked out their mistresses' veils and handkerchiefs, while their mistresses, crouching, read the laundry lists.

"Daughter of Cyrus," said Artystone, crouching

beside Atossa, but on a couch of her own. "Is this handkerchief not marked with your royal A?"

She handed the queen-mother a handkerchief.

The latter snatched at it. The hands of numerous slave-girls were outstretched in order to facilitate the handkerchief's journey from the hand of the one to that of the other queen. But they were not needed. Atossa had seized the handkerchief and was mustering it.

"So it is, Artystone!" said she, half angrily, half amiably, with a smile that was a grin. "These mistakes never end!"

The whip rose and whistled through the air. The slave-girls rhythmically bent their backs and cowered. Suddenly appeased, Atossa laid down the whip.

"Seven times seven linen veils for the night."

"The many different A's are really an inconvenience for the laundresses," said Artystone.

She was gentle and kindly, and had been the wife of whom Darius had been fondest, the fourth in rank. She had been very beautiful, and was still a virgin when he wedded her. And he had had a golden image made of her. Her son was Gobryas, and Gobryas was Mardonius' father. Her second son was Arsames, and thus Mardonius was Xerxes' nephew. He had urged the king to go to war. Arsames, like Mardonius, was a general, and led the Ethiopians. Mardonius, as stated, was married to Xerxes' sister Artozostra, who sat on her couch beside Artystone, and was the latter's niece by marriage.

"Venerable grandmother!" said Artozostra. Although only related by marriage, she resembled her grandmother. The latter, though still not at all old, already was faded—a Persian royal widow is never young—and all the princesses resembled each other, more or less.

"Here are three handkerchiefs of Tyrian purple. They are marked with your very own A."

Artystone, Darius' best-beloved wife, received the handkerchiefs from her niece's hands with a winning gesture. The slave-girls busied themselves with unnecessary passings about of the handkerchiefs.

"Who has a veil of mine with a Sun embroidered in the middle?" Queen Amestris, quite upset, asked the circle.

"Holy, holy, holy!" cried the slave-girls and bowed low or flung themselves down. For the word "Sun" was a holy word.

"I have, royal aunt Amestris!" cried youthful Artaynte, and herself brought the queen the Sun-veil, her young slave-girls following her like fluttering birds.

"I mark my things only with my Sun," said Amestris. "Holy, holy!" murmured the slaves. It sounded like the humming of bees amid the rose-fragrance.

"And yet they are constantly mixed up," Amestris continued. "Artaynte! These handkerchiefs are marked with your A."

"Yes, royal aunt," Artaynte agreed, and took the little pile.

Amestris scrutinized her carefully.

"You are growing beautiful, girl," said the queen somewhat sharply. "See that you do not grow too beautiful."

"No, indeed, royal aunt," said Artaynte, smiling because she did not understand. "Mother is more beautiful than I am."

[38]

"Why is your mother not here?" asked the queen.

"She is sugaring rose-pods, royal aunt."

"Oh," said Amestris, laughing and covetous.

Meanwhile Phaidyme and Parmys, Darius' two other widows, second and third in rank, sat quietly counting their handkerchiefs and veils. There could be no mistake in their case; their marks were a P and a Ph.

Parmys was the daughter of Smerdis, that brother of Cambyses whom he had had murdered, and of Phaidyme. Phaidyme, Queen Amestris' oldest sister, like Atossa, had been compelled to marry pseudo-Smerdis, and she enjoyed nothing more than telling the pretender's story, though everyone at court already knew it by heart. And so Queen Amestris took pleasure in teasing Phaidyme, and thus making herself popular with all the lesser wives and the slave-girls. And now, since she was somewhat fatigued by her weaving—the laundry had been carried off—she called out in a mellifluous, coaxing voice:

"Dearest sister, royal Phaidyme, oldest sister! Do tell us, I beg of you, how it came to be discovered that pseudo-Smerdis was not Smerdis, but a tricky Magian! I beg of you, oldest daughter of Otanes, my father, dearest sister, tell us once more in detail how it all happened."

Queen Amestris made a gesture in the direction of the anterooms which opened off from the side of her couch. There hundreds of concubines were sitting or moving about, surrounded by hundreds of slaves. They were weaving, spinning, embroidering or sugaring the seed-pods of roses. As soon as they saw that Queen Amestris was trying to induce her sister Phaidyme to tell the too well-known tale once more,

[39]

they came hurrying up from every side. Behind the loom and behind the couches of Artozostra and Artaynte was a swarm of heads, large and small, of Persian, Bactrian and Caspian women and girls. There were faces broad and narrow, with pale amber and yellow tea-rose complexions, blue-black, mischievous eyes, under black-painted eyebrows, mutely laughing, mocking little noses and little mouths, all crowded together, too many to count. Even the three other royal windows, Parmys, the true Smerdis' daughter, Darius' best-beloved wife, and Atossa, commanding reverence and inspiring awe, looked secretly and with quiet enjoyment at their fellow widow, who was preparing to tell her tale anew.

Phaidyme began:

"Haven't I told you about it? No? Then, of course, I'll be glad to do so. Well, I, Otanes' daughter, was one of Cambyses' wives, besides Atossa, the daughter of Cyrus, wasn't I?"

Atossa nodded sweetly in agreement. She, too, was gloating over Phaidyme's beginning to tell the story for the hundredth time, and though Phaidyme was younger than she, the old woman thought her actually childish. She herself was anything but that. She only resented no longer being initiated into the latest palace secrets and intrigues, and that was something she could not endure. But the old palace secrets and intrigues had all been part of her life, and in her own despite Cyrus' daughter listened, with lurking eyes and an angrily smiling mouth.

"When Cambyses marched off to Egypt to conquer it . . ." Phaidyme began in a monotonous dragging voice.

She interrupted herself.

[40]

"He was mad, he was half insane. Indeed he was mad, was he not, O daughter of Cyrus?"

"My brother was not always accountable," murmured Atossa who, though it was all a jest, beheld the past rise up before her.

"Yes, he was mad," Phaidyme went on. "For in Memphis he had made a mock of the god Apis, and slew him with his dagger, because he insisted that a god never could be a young bull."

"The gods punished him for it," half instinctively murmured Parmys, the third royal widow. "The sheath of his sword fell away at the same spot in which he struck Apis, and he gave himself a fatal wound in the side."

"It happened in Ecbatana," murmured Atossa. "The oracle had predicted that he would die in Ecbatana. But he had in mind Ecbatana in Media, the city of the seven walls, where he had left his treasures. There, so he believed, he would die when his course was run. But he died in Ecbatana in Syria."

This she murmured inaudibly. The women crowding behind Amestris and her loom listened, while they giggled surreptitiously and were unspeakably happy. They never would have dared to giggle at Atossa, who was so spitefully on the watch.

"Well, then," Phaidyme once more began. "When Cambyses marched to Egypt to conquer it, the Magian Patiseithes, who administered his estates in Susa, hit upon the idea that his brother, who was also named Smerdis, like your father, Parmys, daughter of Smerdis . . ."

Phaidyme nodded in the direction of the couch where Parmys squatted in an expressive pose.

"Yes, my father Smerdis, whom Cambyses had

[41]

murdered by the hand of Prexaspes, because he had dreamed his brother was enthroned on his own throne, and that his head towered into the skies . . ." Parmys reminded herself.

"It happened here," murmured Atossa, "here in the hall of the women."

Before her rose the pictures of the past.

"So this Patiseithes hit upon the idea," Phaidyme monotonously continued, "to have his brother, who also chanced to be named Smerdis, and closely resembled Cambyses' brother . . ." The concubines behind Amestris and the slave-girls behind the concubines, and Amestris behind the loom, all began to writhe and twist with laughter.

". . . proclaimed king in Cambyses' stead. After all, Cambyses was far away, and Smerdis, Patiseithes' brother, was named Smerdis like Cambyses' brother, and closely resembled him. Yet he had no ears. Cyrus, your exalted father, Atossa, had had them cut off for some offence, I no longer remember what offence."

"Poor Phaidyme," Artystone, on Atossa's further side, remarked to her granddaughter Artozostra. "She never knows for which offence he lost his ears, but, after all, Amestris and the concubines should not make so much fun of her."

And at the same time Artystone and youthful Artozostra, who sat opposite her, exchanged merry glances of understanding and mischievous winks because Phaidyme was back at her story again.

"Yet when pseudo-Smerdis," Phaidyme continued, quite undisturbed, "never showed himself to the great lords of the land, and always hid himself in the palace, suspicion was aroused. And my father Otanes was the first who began to suspect . . ."

[42]

Phaidyme paused, in order to crunch some of the candied rose-pods, which the slave-girls offered the queens and princesses on large, round wicker platters, for them to taste.

"The first who began to suspect," Phaidyme went on, as she chewed the rose-pods, "that the man who called himself Smerdis was a cheat. Then my father questioned me with regard to Smerdis, with whom I slept what times you or the other women did not sleep with him. Was it not so, Atossa?" Atossa frowned gloomily. Anger and dislike prompted a biting reply, but together with all the others she was secretly deriving too much enjoyment from the fact that Phaidyme was once more telling her story. So she smiled an assent with hypocritical sweetness, while her suspicious glances sought to pierce the loom to discover whether Queen Amestris and the other women were doing more than just making a mock of Phaidyme.

"But I had never seen the true Smerdis, Cambyses' brother, and your father, Parmys . . ."

"Yes, my father," replied Parmys, in a fury. "It was shameful of Cambyses to murder him."

"Tut, tut, tut," said Atossa with imperious haughtiness. "Cambyses was my brother and husband, Parmys. I'll ask you not to forget it."

But Amestris called out:

"I beg of you to continue, oldest sister, dear Phaidyme! What happened then and what did our father Otanes ask you?"

"He asked me whether I could not consult with the other women, and with you as well, Atossa. But I never saw you. For pseudo-Smerdis kept all the women separated from each other in different apartments."

[43]

Atossa remembered it. She recalled that she had
been treated like a prisoner, she, the daughter of
Cyrus, she, Cambyses' sister and wife, she, whom
pseudo-Smerdis had taken to wife together with all
the rest of the harem after Cambyses' death. She
also remembered Otanes' secret questionings and her
intrigues. But she recalled as well that it had been
impossible for the imprisoned women to get in touch
with each other, in spite of all the scheming of con
cubines and slaves.

"And then . . ." said Phaidyme.

"Here it comes," thought Amestris maliciously.

"Here it comes," said the women behind her and
giggled.

"Then my father, by the mouth of his secret spy
ordered me to make sure that Smerdis had ears. For
the true Smerdis had ears, but pseudo-Smerdis had
none. Cyrus had had them cut off, I really don'
remember for which offence."

From the couches and from behind the loom came
the sound of laughter and giggling.

"It was very dangerous for me," Phaidyme went
on, quite unconcerned, "to convince myself whether
or no Smerdis had ears. Yet I did so in order to dis
cover whether Smerdis was Smerdis. Once, after
had again shared his bed . . ."

All the women drew mysteriously closer, as
though to drink the weighty words about to fall
from Phaidyme's lips.

"Smerdis fell asleep after love's game had been
played."

"And then, sister?"

"And then, Phaidyme?"

"And then, and then, royal Phaidyme?" cried the
concubines and the queen.

"Then I groped . . ." Phaidyme's hands
ketched a groping gesture.

"And then I felt, I felt—that Smerdis had no ears
under his long locks."

There was an outburst of feminine laughter. But
t was at once hushed.

"What is the matter?" Phaidyme asked in sur-
rise .

"Nothing, oldest sister," said Amestris. "One
of the slave-girls standing behind us has fallen into
he cooking fruit."

"It is an outrage," cried Atossa, annoyed by the
overloud laughter. "Where is she, Amestris? Where
s she? I want to see her. I want her. Here!"

Amestris hurriedly gave an order.

"Bring her to me! Make haste!" called Atossa.

It was a matter of only a few moments. Out on
he portico, where the women were busy with their
beauty lotions, their attars and their preserving, a
ew of them had hurriedly poured the contents of a
great copper kettle over the head of a slave-girl who
was the butt of all their jests. The girl screamed as
he warm mush flowed over her face and breasts.
The other women pushed her into the room.

"Here she is, Allhighest," giggled the women, tug-
ging the dripping slave-girl into Atossa's presence.

The whip whistled through the air.

"So you have to spoil preserves?" shrilled Atossa,
and struck her again and again. "Let the stupid
wench be crucified!"

The Chief Eunuch Ogoas appeared in the entrance
to the hall, between the couches of Amestris and
Artozostra.

"O Queen of Persia!" He had a falsetto voice.
"Couriers have arrived from Celænæ, from the King

[45]

of Kings and the princes of Persia. Behold, here ar
their letters!"

He pointed to a basket which two other eunuch
dragged in. It was the royal mail. To an accom
paniment of officious ceremonial on the part of th
eunuchs, who actually crawled with subservience
great letter rolls and writing tablets from Xerxes and
Masistes, Atossa's second son, sealed with golder
seals, were handed out to Amestris and to Atossa
together with missives from the latter's two neph
ews, her nephews once removed and her grandsons
all having commands in the Persian army. Arty
stone received wax tablets from her great-grandson
Mardonius and Arsames, the latter general of th
Ethiopian troops. Parmys was similarly remembered
by her son Ariomardus, commanding the Moscians
Artozostra by her husband Mardonius, Artaynte by
her father Masistes. Her mother Artaxixa left he
cooking on the portico to see whether letters had
come for her. Phaidyme, too, had received a lette
from her father Otanes.

"Is there no letter from Otanes for me, his daugh
ter and Persia's queen?" Amestris angrily inquired

Among all these letters which the eunuchs, crawl
ing with reverence over the bare mosaic floor betweer
the circle of couches, were separating, they managed
to find that from Otanes to his daughter, the queen
and gave it to her.

There was great excitement. The queens and
princesses broke the seals, and the concubines and
slave-girls crowded together behind them, mad with
curiosity.

Atossa began to read aloud a sentence from Xerxes
letter, narrowing her near-sighted eyes behind ;
ground beryl-stone, which served her as an eyeglass

That is, she narrowed only one eye, the other she shut completely: "Allhighest royal Mother, Daughter of Cyrus, Wife of my never-to-be-forgoten father, Darius!" Atossa read. "As I am about to pass over the bridge of boats across the Hellespont with my tremendous armies, I, your son, the King of Kings, inform you that I am in need of concubines and lesser bedfellows, of whom only a limited number has accompanied us."

"The king writes me the same," cried Amestris.

And it turned out, as a multitude of voices insisted on being heard, that all the Persian generals—their sons, brothers, nephews, uncles, grandsons and nephews once removed—informed the four royal widows and the queen that they had not brought enough mopsies along with the army to be able to cross the Hellespont. They wrote this with premeditation. Not alone did Xerxes write thus to Amestris; Masistes wrote so to Artaxixa, and Ariomardus to Parmys. All the men wrote the same thing to their mothers and wives. For if they had merely ordered the Chief Eunuch to send them concubines and bedfellows before they left Sardis and crossed the Hellespont, there can be no question but that rebellion and a women's war would have flared up among the queens and princesses. Yet now, since the king and the princes all informed them of their sorry case, now that they left it to *them* to decide which concubines and bed-slaves among the thousands of women in the Susa palace they would instruct the eunuchs to send on, the royal women were flattered and disarmed. It is true that Artaxixa, Artaynte's very beautiful mother—the tip of her nose had been reddened by the preserved fruits whose

[47]

sweetness she had so conscientiously been testing
while they cooked—called out:

"My Masistes never has enough bedfellows. Ah
Artaynte, my daughter, what an insatiable father the
Sun has bestowed on you!"

"Holy, holy, holy!" cried all the women.

"And what a husband has he given me! Child,
come and attend to your preserving. What do you
mean by hunkering lazily on a couch instead of help-
ing your mother preserve rose-pods?" She pulled
Artaynte down from the couch and took her place
on it. Artaynte pouted, but even so she was en-
chantingly lovely. Pouting she disappeared into
the portico. Rose-fragrance and sweet odours
steamed into the room.

Amestris ordered her loom put aside.

"Allhighest!" she called out respectfully to Atossa.
"Are you in favour of our consulting together as to
which concubines and slave-girls we shall select for
our husbands, sons and nephews?"

"Have Ogoas join us in that case!"

The queen beckoned the Chief Eunuch to join
their circle.

The Chief Eunuch beckoned fourteen other eunuchs, who made up his suite, to accompany him.

Atossa and Amestris sent away all the concubines
and slave-girls.

Yet they did not go far, but peeped and eaves-
dropped behind the columns of the portico.

The couches occupied by the women were thereupon shoved closer together. The consultation began.

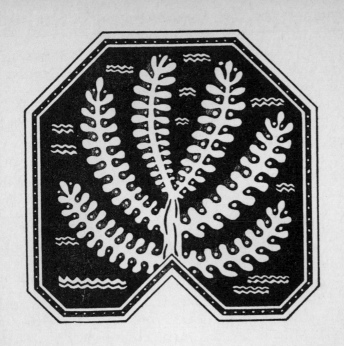

## CHAPTER VII

## THE PLANE-TREE

Two days' journey from Sardis, where Xerxes and his generals had been waiting all winter, until Athos should have been cut through and the bridge of boats across the Hellespont completed, the highway branched out. One road led to Caria, the other to Sardis, the capital of Lydia.

The road to Sardis runs over a bridge across the Mæander, and past the town of Callatebos. It is a place where the succulent juice of plants is gathered in quantity. Its traders prepared a delicate and fragrant honey-paste out of the heart of wheat and the sap of the myrica or tamarisk.

A caravan of mules, laden with this bayberry honey in great pots and pails, was on its way to Sardis, when it passed an enormous plane-tree. The plane-tree had already put forth its new leaves, that were outlined against the pale blue skies of spring in their glimmering golden-green as though cut with scissors, and up and down before the plane-tree, with furious steps, paced an Immortal, a giant of a man.

The Immortals formed the very flower of the Life Guards of the King of Kings. Under the command of Hydarnes, son of Hydarnes, the Immortals numbered ten thousand picked soldiers. Splendidly accoutred, they made a magnificent appearance. They were called the Immortals because they always numbered exactly ten thousand. When one was slain or fell ill, his place was immediately taken by a new reversionary.

Furiously the Immortal strode to and fro before the enormous plane-tree as the honey-caravan came slowly along the dusty highroad. It was a sandy, rocky countryside. There were the blue hills, disappearing in the distance. There was the blue sky round about. There stood the enormous plane-tree by the highway. And there was the Immortal, furiously pacing his beat.

"Hey!" the Immortal called out to the leader of the caravan. "Where are you going?"

"To Sardis," replied the latter. "To the army, to the court, to the king, with this bayberry honey. Is an Immortal always standing guard here by the plane-tree?"

"I don't know whether an Immortal is always standing guard here by the plane-tree," the soldier answered in a rage, "but I know for a fact that this Immortal has already been standing guard here by

ST. JOSEPH'S COLLEGE

this plane-tree for two days and a night, and that they've forgotten to relieve him. Are they all crazy in Sardis? They've completely forgotten me. I'm worn out. I've had nothing to eat for three days. I'm dying of thirst. Last night I sank down exhausted against this plane-tree and fell asleep. May Ahriman and all his devils take it to hell, this double-damned plane-tree!"

He shook his fist at it. But the plane-tree continued to stand as before in all the tremendous beauty and strength of its silver trunk, spreading out its heavy boughs and unfolding new leaves. When Xerxes had passed by the plane-tree on his way to Sardis he had greatly admired it, had called it a queen among trees, and had embraced it as a royal brother. Curious artistic impulses often awakened in Xerxes. The plane-tree's beauty had moved him. Thereupon he had commanded that the plane-tree be hung with chains of honour and armlets, chains of honour about the trunk, armlets about its branches. And he had left one of the Immortals behind on sentry-go at the plane.

The whole winter long the sentry had been relieved every day from Sardis. And it was a long march from Sardis to the plane. But this Immortal seemed to have been forgotten. There was no inn anywhere near. There was only the endless, dusty white road, the blue mountain range in the distance, the blue sky arching over the rocky landscape. There was the plane-tree, loaded with its chains of honour and its armlets. And there was the furious Immortal.

"To hell with it!" he repeated. "Caravan leader, I'm going off with you!"

[51]

"But how about the chains of honour and the armlets?" cried the leader of the caravan.

The Immortal swore.

"They've forgotten the plane-tree in Sardis," he shouted. "I'll fetch the armlets and chains of honour down from the tree."

"Immortal, have you lost your mind?" cried the leader of the caravan. "They'll nail you to a cross!" The muleteers likewise uttered cries of horror. But the Immortal seemed to have gone mad. He tore the chains of honour from the trunk, and climbed to a lower bough to detach its armlet. The leader and his muleteers watched, petrified with terror. For the Immortal now had climbed high up into the plane-tree and was stripping its branches of their armlets.

"Catch!" he cried as he rudely flung down the honorific decorations.

He climbed down, staggering from exhaustion, and gathered up the golden ornaments.

"Here," said he, as he thrust an armlet upon the caravan leader. "This is for you, and these two are for your muleteers, and the rest of them are mine. Take me along with you, among your pots and pails of bayberry honey." The muleteers helped the prince of a fellow into a cart. There the Immortal's gigantic limbs joggled about most uncomfortably among the big pails, and he nearly fainted. Yet before the caravan, loitering and swaying, got under way again, with much cracking of whips and loud objurgation on the part of the muleteers and the leader, the Immortal shook his fist at the plane and cried:

"You god-damn plane-tree! You god-damn plane-tree, you!"

The plane-tree made no reply. It did not even seem to notice that it had been stripped of all the decorations of honour bestowed on it by the King of Kings, and, quite unmoved, omnipotent in its beauty and power, it flung its broad crown of leaves to the skies.

## CHAPTER VIII

## WHIPS ON THE HELLESPONT

FROM Sardis Xerxes sent out heralds to all parts of Greece, with the exception of Attica and Lacedæmonia. Demanding earth and water—the symbol of voluntary submission to his will—he sent heralds to all the cities, to command that supplies be made ready and a meal prepared wherever the King of Kings might appear with his armies. Earth and water, in his day, had been denied Darius, Xerxes' never-to-be-forgotten father.

Meanwhile thousands of builders worked on the bridge of boats across the Hellespont, between Abydos and Sestos. The strait in that spot was very narrow, no more than seven stadia in width, but ran like a broad river between rough, rocky shores. The Egyptians fastened the ships together with cables of byblus cord, but the experienced Phœnicians gave preference to flaxen ropes.

A severe storm, that for several days had spent its fury on land and sea, tore asunder the byblus as well as the flaxen cables and let the ships dash themselves to pieces against each other. Then the storm ceased, as though satisfied, and the ocean became calm as a lake. Flowing between the rocks, disappearing in a blue haze beneath a heaven of radiant blue, the Hellespont seemed no more than an innocent stream. an idyllic watercourse under vernal southern skies.

The winds were just as peaceful as when, long ago, they had let Hero and Leander perish on the selfsame spot—when they had swallowed Leander, swimming to Hero's tower, and Hero, who cast herself from the tower into the sea. They drove on the lightly curling waves in a barely perceptible manner.

In spite of this the Hellespont was to be punished.

Xerxes would also gladly have chastised the winds. But they blew where they listed and it was not easy to lash them. Yet the Hellespont was to get a flogging. In the sight of the soldiers and the townsfolk who came crowding up to look on, Xerxes' hangmen flogged the Hellespont and counted aloud the three hundred lashes they gave it. The torturers branded the water with red-hot irons. When the irons hissed in the lightly curling waves of the Hellespont and the latter merely foamed slightly under the blows of the lashes and then indifferently continued on their murmuring course, the townsfolk began to laugh.

Xerxes' sergeants cast furious glances round about and roughly cried:

"Scum!"

Then the townsfolk stopped laughing. A herald with a far-carrying voice read aloud from a roll that he unfolded: "Sweet waters, salt waters, your Master chastises you because you have dared to oppose and to insult him. Xerxes, the King of Kings, will cross you in one way or another. No one shall ever offer up a sacrifice to you. For you are merely a deceitful, salty river."

The Hellespont curled on its way, murmuring that it was no river, but a strait, though a very narrow one. But the hangmen did not understand the Hellespont. They cut off the heads of the builders of the destroyed bridge, and other builders tried their skill on another bridge of boats.

They tied triremes to each other and vessels of fifty oars. There were three hundred on the western, and three hundred fourteen on the eastern side. The first vessels turned their flanks toward the Propontis, the others, pointing toward the Ægean Sea, drifted with the stream, so that their cables stretched more tautly. Anchors were cast off from the vessels. This time double cables, on tremendous wooden drums fixed on the shore, held together the ships. The byblus-rope cables were stretched by fours, the flaxen ropes by twos. These latter were the strongest, and their every elbow-length weighed a talent.

When the ships lay thus firmly bound together, broad boards were sawn, planed, and laid side by side across the ships on heavy wooden underpinnings, while the rope cables were drawn taut and the wooden boardwalk was covered with sand. Board fences were put up on the sides so that the horses and pack animals would not shy by catching sight of the not always lightly curling, but often heavily storming Hellespont.

The Phœnicians were proud of their ropes. For they wore slightly but never gave. Yet the Egyptians insisted that their ropes were no less good.

The bridge over the Hellespont was completed.

And Mount Athos had been cut through.

They were two imposing pieces of work.

Xerxes was informed of the achievement.

He left Sardis with his army.

While he was on the way to Abydos the sun grew dark in the clear, cloudless sky, and night fell in the midst of day.

The Persians knelt in the fields on either side of the highway, praying, and calling on Ormuzd and on Mithra.

Xerxes begged the Magians who accompanied him to interpret the eclipse.

They told him that the Sun, although the god of Persia—the god of the Persians—did not foretell the future of Persia, but the future and the downfall of Greece.

The moon foretold the future of Persia.

The sun came out. The endless army streamed gratefully along in the pallid, indefinite light of day.

CHAPTER IX

## THE MILLIONAIRE'S MISTAKE

A T THE first resting-place Pythius, the wealthy Lydian who had offered his entire fortune to the King of Kings at Celænæ, came to meet Xerxes with a great following and a thousand and one ceremonies.

Xerxes received him in the mansion hurriedly furnished and tapestried by his household officials, in which he meant to spend the night, and—a kindly smile playing about his blue-black beard—bade him say what was on his mind. For he thought the Lydian had again come to offer him hard cash. With humble movements of arm and hand Pythius seated himself on a tabouret opposite Xerxes who, no matter where he might be, always found a throne at his disposal. Various thrones accompanied Xerxes on his journey.

Encouraged by the kindly smile, Pythius said: "Great Despot! May I venture to beg of you a favour, one you can easily grant, and which would greatly benefit me were you to grant it?"

"Let me hear your plea," replied Xerxes, with a smile. He still thought that money would once more be offered him humbly and in flowery terms, and had in mind to reply, in flowery terms, but not humbly:

"Pythius! You have given me much. Yet I shall be just like my never-to-be-forgotten father, Darius. I will grant whatever you may ask."

Xerxes thought: he will ask me again whether I want his coined money, a few talents of silver, or four or five millions of golden staters.

Pythius breathed more freely and said:

"Basileus! I have five sons to depend upon in my old age. The military law compels them all to follow you on your campaign to Greece. Have pity on my white hairs! Let me keep my oldest! Excuse him, him only, from service! That is my plea to your Majesty. Permit that he remain with me, to administer my estates!" And old Pythius clasped his hand in entreaty, while a smile played about his grey beard. He thought his case already won.

But Xerxes started up, wild with rage:

"What? No talents of silver? No golden staters? Miserable wretch! How now? I go to Greece with my young sons, my brothers, brothers-in-law and nephews, and you—my slave—dare to mention your son? You should have been com-

[59]

pelled to follow me with all your household, your women and children and all your slaves, who are all my property! For what is there that anyone among my subjects can own in particular? Know now that the spirit of man thrones here within this ear!"

Passionately he pointed to his ear.

"When he hears something pleasant," Xerxes went on, still pointing to his ear, "he is pleased, and his pleasure spreads throughout his body. When he hears something unpleasant"—his index finger still threatening to pierce his eardrum—"he turns angry and fury seizes him. Although in the beginning you so conducted yourself that you won my approval, yet you were never so long-suffering as I, your king, have been. I am convinced that you have hidden many talents of silver, and who can say how many millions of golden staters. In spite of this, as a proof of my royal gratitude, I will not treat you harshly. You have asked me for one son out of the five. I give you four, but the fifth, your favourite, I shall punish as I see fit."

And Xerxes commanded that Pythius' oldest son be seized.

The boy was delivered to the executioners and cut in two by the sword. One half of his body was laid down on each side of the road to Abydos.

The following morning Xerxes continued his march with his army, and generals, officers, sergeants and men in the ranks cast shy glances, to right and left, at the bloody halves of the body.

For hours the infantry kept passing, the hoofs of the cavalry rang out. White clouds of dust whirled up.

After the hour of noon came the venerable Pythius, lamenting, together with many old, chosen friends, all millionaires like himself.

Then there was loud wailing, and the aged millionaires took the two halves of the body, that lay on either side of the road, and joined them together on a bier, which was covered with a saffron-yellow cloth. And the wealthy ancients carried back the bier, whispering among themselves: "Had Pythius only been satisfied to pay the king the regular war-tax due, and not given him all his ready money!"

"All his ready money?"

"Nearly all his ready money. If only he had given no more than we gave."

"He could have enjoyed his oldest son for a long time to come."

"As we may, in the case of our first-born, should they return victorious with Xerxes."

So the old millionaires, who had all surrendered their sons but not their hard cash, carried the bier back to the city, lamenting as they went.

## CHAPTER X

## TROY TOWERS

THE host flowed from Sardis toward Abydos on the Hellespont. Camels, dromedaries, mules led the way. They carried chests and containers—an endless caravan. Then followed the soldiers of all the nations subject to the King of Kings. They made up more than half the host. They followed each other, with their generals, officers and sergeants, in well-nigh disordered masses, held together only by the snapping whips. Then there was a gap.

It was a long gap, during which the dust of the road settled again. Then, stately and keeping the same pace, followed thousands of horsemen, picked soldiery, chosen from among all Xerxes' Persian subjects. And after them thousands of footmen, armed with spears whose points were inclined downward, marching in parade step, the flower of the infantry, and after these came the ten sacred horses.

They were Nisæan steeds. They hailed from the Nisæan plain in Media. There was located the splendid stud farm comprising a hundred fifty thousand horses, the noblest and largest on earth, white or black, snow-white or pitch-black, and whoever saw them trotting across the Nisæan plain thought he behold the steeds of the gods—steeds of the foaming ocean or storm-driven clouds, steeds whose nostrils breathed flame, steeds with flashing eyes, arched necks, tossing manes and waving tails. Whoever had seen those hundred fifty thousand horses trotting across the Nisæan plain had beheld an incredibly beautiful sight, a living ocean, an ever-moving heaven of clouds that had sunk to earth. The ten sacred horses, magnificently caparisoned and adorned with aigrettes of feathers, had been chosen from among this herd. They followed the infantry, led by grooms of noble birth.

Then came the sacred chariot of Zeus. It was empty, but it was drawn by ten white horses, and the driver followed the horses on foot. For no one was allowed to enter the chariot. Zeus, the Zeus of the Persians, the Persian godhead, now and again invisibly took his place therein.

Xerxes followed in his war chariot drawn by a team of Nisæan steeds, and his charioteer marched afoot. He was a brother of Amestris. His name was Patiramphes, and Otanes was his father.

Next came Xerxes' *haxamaxa*, the covered carriage in which he stretched out when he had wearied of standing proudly in his chariot.

After it came a thousand lance-bearers. The tips of their lances pointed upward. Golden apples shone beneath the steel. At their heels rode a thousand horsemen, the pick of the cavalry.

Then came the ten thousand Immortals.

All these horsemen and footmen glittered in gilded helmets and armour flexibly adjusted to their limbs, in armlets and cuisses, with huge shields, bows, swords and lances. On all of them, lightly or heavily, gold lay like a sea of light. A thousand among the Immortals carried lances adorned with golden pomegranates, the other nine thousand bore pomegranates of silver, and the gold and silver seemed a dazzling glory above their helmeted heads. This glory was reflected in their eyes as though in small, and in their bucklers as though in large mirrors. About the men's nostrils played a reflection, gold, silver and blue. For the sun, which glowed in the heavy azure sky, was reflected by all, by the pomegranates and the apples, by the shields and by the lance-tips. When the horses snorted and reared, their white or black manes fluttered festally, like splendid standards, above all the radiance.

Once more there was a gap of two stadia.

And then came the tremendous main body of the host, hour-long, marching without formation, and disciplined by the cracking whips and the sergeants' curses.

In the afternoon the air grew heavier and more oppressive. The army left Lydia and crossed into Mysia, traversed the town of Carena and passed Adramyttium, and Antrandus, the ancient Pelasgian city. It left Mount Ida behind it on the left, and on the evening of the same day marched across the Homeric fields. The better educated among the generals divined Troy in the distance. A fierce pride fevered Xerxes' blood. He spied through the curtains of his haxamaxa to catch a glimpse of the famous ruins.

All he saw was hillsides wrapped in haze beneath a black, tragic sky filled with chasing clouds. A halt was ordered. The army was to camp on the slopes of Mount Ida. For the men were greatly wearied by the march. A fearful storm broke when night was darkest. Following the eclipse, many thought this an evil omen.

Attracted by the masses of metal, and running down the flashing lances, the lightning that night slew countless horses and men.

The following evening the army camped on the shores of the Scamander. Since leaving Sardis the soldiers had scarce been able to quench their thirst. Though swollen with rain, the river hardly yielded enough water for all the men, horses and pack animals. After all these had drunk naught was left in the river bed but slime, which soon dried and then split asunder in the heavy penetrating sunshine.

Xerxes visited the ruins of Troy, King Priam's castle of Pergamus. He had himself guided about, and recited verses from the *Iliad* in wretched Greek. He was deeply moved by his own sudden artistic impulse. On the eve of his great undertaking he felt uneasy amid these surroundings where the Trojans had been destroyed, and their town had gone up in flame. On the Trojan citadel there was still, as in heroic times, a temple of Pallas Athene. There Xerxes sacrificed a thousand buffalo to the goddess. The army devoured their flesh. The Magians poured libations to the *manes* of the Trojan heroes. That night, when again a storm began to rage, there was rioting in the army. Many soldiers fled in panic fear.

Xerxes heard nothing about it.

At dawn the army resumed its march on Abydos.

## CHAPTER XI

## ARROGANCE

I T WAS a day of radiant sunlight. From a hill-
top, from a high marble throne towering above
the numerous seats occupied by his captains,
Xerxes reviewed his army and his fleet. The fleet,
with its triremes and longer vessels, covered the
Hellespont as far as eye could reach to east and west.
The army was preparing to march across the double
bridge of boats. It glittered on the strand before the
town of Abydos in lozenges of radiance, square and
oblong, in the sparks which the sun coaxed from
shields, spears and helmets. Seen from the marble
throne, it was a tremendously impressive spectacle.

[67]

Over all the land the host bloomed and glowed like endless fields of radiant gold and silver sheaves, sheaves that were weapons. Over all the sea, whose golden-blue waters rolled and foamed, the glittering ships rocked like graceful beasts of fable with innumerable teeming feet, represented by the lightly moving oars. And Xerxes' heart swelled with pride and haughtiness, so that in his joy and gratitude he cried aloud to heaven. Yet scarcely had he done so when he seemed to be seized with terror became of his own greatness, and his jubilation ended in a convulsive fit of sobbing and an endless flow of tears.

"What troubles you, O nephew and king?" asked Artabanus, who despite his years had thus far accompanied the army. "I thought you had but just cried out to the gods for joy, and now you weep like a child?"

On his throne Xerxes, behind the backs of his captains who sat reviewing the troops, convulsively grasped his uncle by the arm and whispered into his ear:

"When I reflect on the transience of human life, uncle, I weep at the thought that in a hundred years not a single man of these hundreds of thousands who compose my army and my fleet will survive, and a well-nigh dizzying feeling of emptiness overcomes me."

Artabanus mustered Xerxes. He was acquainted with his sentimental impulses, his weaknesses. They were at times of an æsthetic, at others of a philosophic nature. And they had a thousand other shades as well. This time his excess was not æsthetically motived; as in the case of the plane-tree. It was quite specifically philosophic, and Uncle Artabanus, who was himself philosophically inclined, thought it incumbent on him to reply in the same strain, the more so since he sensed almost with apprehension how Xerxes crowded close to him, and how his hand still clutched the avuncular arm.

"In the course of our lives," said the uncle, in a mournful, broken voice, "we experience things far more terrible than death. Life is short; nevertheless, among all these hundreds of thousands there is not one—not a man on earth—who has not once or more than once wished to die. Men take all their annoyances, their illnesses, sufferings and disappointments too seriously not to have life seem too long to them, now and again, no matter how brief its span."

"I, too, on occasion, have longed to die," Xerxes thought proper to answer, though he no longer recalled when. "Yet now I wish to live. For all this"—he pointed to the great host now radiantly deploying in the sunlight, to the fleet on the water— "is my pride and my joy. Tell me, uncle! Now that the dream appeared to you as clearly and irrefutably as it did to me, do your original doubts still persist? Would you be able, even now, to advise me to forego this war against Greece? Speak without reservation, I beg of you!"

"King," replied Artabanus, "may our dream have well advised us both. Yet in spite of all, I still fear two things at this glorious moment."

"Which things?" queried Xerxes, on whom these words, following upon his philosophic impulse, made a strong impression.

"Land."

"Land?"

"And water."

"And water? Be more specific, uncle. Land,

water? Are you reproaching my host with lack of numbers? my fleet with lack of power? Do you advise that I call in further levies, that I build more ships?"

Xerxes' blue-black beard almost touched his uncle's grey-black one, as the king, seated, still clung to the arm of Artabanus, standing.

"King," answered Artabanus. "Whoso in his right mind could ask you to levy more men or build more ships? Behold the soldiery teeming on the plain and along the strand! Behold the ships teeming on the sea, that seems like a river. O King! I fear land and water, but not because your host is too small or your fleet too inferior. Both are too great, too great. They represent the ultimate degree of human power. Where will you find harbours spacious enough to shelter these thousands of vessels when the Peloponnesian tempests threaten? Where will you find the grain to feed all these men in their hundreds of thousands? I fear the land and I fear the sea, O King! You will be at the mercy of the skies, whence blow the winds, and at the mercy of earth, whence springs the corn. You have no spacious harbours on the coasts of Thrace and Macedonia, and though the order were given in all the lands through which the army marches, still enough grain could not be grown to feed your hundreds of thousands."

Xerxes did not reply. He was pale and he let his glances stray almost timidly over his unmeasurable power.

"If the grain grow and the winds are kind," Artabanus continued, "then, O king, you will become insatiable. You will wish to go on and on. You will want to possess all Europe, all that lies off yonder in the distance, in the mysterious reaches of the West. Your ambition will become boundless."

"That is possible," murmured Xerxes softly to himself.

And then it seemed as though his former impulse and its after-mood had suddenly vanished. His eyes, roaming restlessly about, were replete with the vision of a hitherto unexampled might. Asia was his. Europe would be his. His was the earth, and the skies were his to be. His would be the winds, obedient to his sceptre. His would be the grain, and its ears would bow to him in their fulness. Those Greeks, that wretched little people yonder, he would tread in the dust. An immeasurable emotion swelled within him and caused him to smile silently. Round about the throne, yet so far removed that they could not hear, his guards, the Immortals, stood motionless, like gigantic armoured statues. Before him were aligned the glittering backs of his many captains. All was so quantitative, so radiant, so tremendous. Something enormous already had been achieved. But its might should wax still greater. It would comprise all this, and all else that was by any means attainable.

Again Xerxes smiled amiably, condescendingly, and thinking himself invincible, he repeated:

"It may be, uncle, that what you say is possible. Yet if I were to take everything into consideration I would never act. Is it not better courageously to dare the deed, and of one's own free will endure half the troubles the deed may entail, than allow one's self to be condemned to inaction because of premature misgivings? Man is never sure of anything. The man of courage, as a rule, gains that for which he strives, while the tardy and circumspect seldom attain their life's goal."

Xerxes' eyes were filled with the splendour of his glory, his soul with pride in the magnificent spectacle of his power unfolded before him. He heard himself utter his well-phrased sentences with deep satisfaction. He had released his uncle's arm. Sure of himself, he continued:

"How mighty we Persians have become! If my ancestors, maternal and paternal, had devoted as much time to thought and reflection as you, uncle, the fame of the Persians would not be so great! Our empire has grown great in danger. The greater the enterprise, the greater the danger. We shall suffer no famine. We need fear neither land nor water, uncle. We shall conquer all Europe."

Artabanus realized that there was nothing left for him to say by way of advice or dissuasion. Nevertheless, he remarked:

"Only this one thing, Xerxes, before we say farewell, and I return to Susa: Beware of the Ionians!"

Xerxes laughed.

"Beware of the Ionians!" repeated Artabanus. "Do not lead them into the field against their own blood-brethren. They are not necessary to our numerical superiority. If they march with us they will be either the most contemptible or the most estimable of all peoples. The most contemptible if they bring their country under our yoke, the most estimable if they fight for their freedom. We may regard their unworthiness with indifference. Their worthiness may be a great disadvantage to us."

Xerxes laughed.

"Have no fear, uncle!" he said. "I place full confidence in the Ionians. Return to Susa and rule over

[72]

my empire and my house. I bestow on you my crown and my sceptre."

Xerxes could say things of this sort in an admirable manner. Upon his uncle, the philosopher, when he spoke in this way Xerxes always made a great impression with his proud smile, the regal motion of his arm, and the graceful gesture of his hand. It must be his arrogance which thus harmoniously alternated with gentler moods in his soul, thought his uncle.

The review, with its deploy of army divisions, seemed to have come to an end. For the captains who sat in front of the throne all rose and approached the king.

And Xerxes himself rose and said:

"Persians! In view of the magnificent spectacle which has just been unrolled before our eyes, I charge you with the duty never to let fade the glory of the immortally famous deeds of my exalted ancestors, and of my never-to-be-forgotten father Darius!"

Xerxes made an eloquent speech, to which the captains listened, but as to whose tenor the soldiers assembled on the plain, the ships and the strand might only venture to surmise.

## CHAPTER XII

## THE NUMBERING OF THE HOST

THE army was to cross the Hellespont the following day. The generals waited until sunrise. On the bridge of ships clouds of smoke rose from enormous bronze censers. Myrtle had been scattered over the planking, laurel branches had been wound about the fences and the high palisades. When the sun rose the king, accompanied by his generals, stepped on the bridge. In the midst of his Magians he adored the Sun. He poured the ritual libation from a golden goblet and cried:

"O Sun! Turn away from me all that might prevent Europe, to its utmost limits, from falling to Persia!"

The Magians repeated the prayer. Then Xerxes with a lofty gesture flung into the sea the golden goblet and the sacrificial ewer. And next he allowed a curved sword to glide from his hands into the water.

About him it was whispered that he wished to appease the Hellespont after his flagellation and branding.

The crossing began: it lasted seven days and seven nights. During these days Xerxes, after he himself with his ten thousand Immortals, the sacred chariot, and his bodyguard of lance-bearers had crossed the bridge, saw his army march past on the farther shore.

On the eastern bridge of ships the footmen and horsemen of Asia passed over into Europe.

On the western bridge crossed the pack animals with their chests and containers, and the palanquins with the many secondary wives and the concubines who had been sent along from Susa.

While Xerxes, sitting his throne on the strand of Sestos, beheld the endless ranks pass one after the other before his eyes, a man of Sestos, as though bereft of his senses, cried out to him:

"O Zeus! You, Zeus! Why in the likeness of Xerxes, King of the Persians, do you drag with you so many men to destroy Greece? You could destroy it without them."

Xerxes laughed proudly.

In the very midst of the host a mare dropped a rabbit. How unmistakable was the miracle! It was hardly necessary for the Magians to interpret it. It was as plain as the nose on one's face. The great enterprise would yield but a trifling success; it might even end in flight. And a mule cast a hermaphrodite foal. This miracle was harder to explain, and yet . . .

Xerxes laughed these wonders to scorn. His proud fleet was now steering past the inlets of the coast. His army, marching through the Melas river—whose waters it drank leaving a dry bed behind,—pushed on along a necessarily western detour to Minos, and then poured into the plain of Doriscus, which stretches down to the sea.

Through that plain runs the Hebrus, a mighty river which the host did not at once drink dry. West of it rise the palace and citadel of Doriscus, where Darius had left a garrison when he fared forth to battle with the Scythians. The plain and the sea-scape seemed to Xerxes better suited to hold a second and more comprehensive review of his soldiers and fleet than had been possible on the strand of Abydos and the ridiculously narrow Hellespont.

He felt that he could breathe more freely, that his army and fleet could breathe more freely, as though he had already conquered a larger slice of the world.

The ships were aligned between Thasus and Samothrace, while the King of Kings ordered the multitudes of his host to march past the citadel.

All in all, they numbered one million seven hundred thousand men. A body of ten thousand soldiers had been crowded closely together under the lash, a circle drawn around them and a wall erected, reaching to the height of a man's navel. Then the detachment had been let out and another let in, without counting them. And thus the count of one million seven hundred thousand had been made. And now the soldiers marched by in parade.

[76]

First came the Persians.  They wore pointed felt head-dresses, called tiaras, long, multi-coloured coats with snug-fitting sleeves, breastplates with iron scales like those of a fish, and long, close-fitting trousers.  They looked handsome and supple.  Their uniforms made them appear slender, and showed athletic figures in youthful outline to the best advantage.  Their osier bucklers, a quiver attached to the lower ends, were slung across their shoulders.  They showed as long graceful disks.  They had excessively long bows, their cane arrows were long, and daggers swung rhythmically above their right thighs.

The grandee Otanes, Queen Amestris' father and one of the seven Persian nobles who had put Darius on the throne, although well along in years, led them on horseback.

The Medes followed the Persians.  They were equipped in the same manner, for already in Cyrus' day the Persians had taken over the costume of the vanquished Medes.  Tigranes, the Achæmenian, rode at their head.

The Cissians, accoutred like the Medes, save that they wore a metal mitre, came next.  Anaphes, son of Otanes, the queen's brother and Xerxes' brother-in-law, led them on horseback.

The Hyrcanians, armed like the Cissians, followed them.  Megapanus, satrap of Babylon, rode at their head.

The Assyrians followed the Hyrcanians.  They wore helmets curiously wrought of strips of brass.  And they had cuirasses of linen, linen in an eighteen-fold ply, steeped in salt and wine lees.  No arrow could pierce this armour.  They carried wooden clubs knotted with iron, and the Chaldeans went similarly equipped. Otaspes, son of Artachæus, led them on horseback.

The Bactrians followed the Assyrians. Their arrows were quite short. The Sacae, who were Scythians, followed the Bactrians. Their arrows were very broad. Hystaspes, son of Darius and of Atossa, Xerxes' brother, led the well-nigh countless horde of both races on horseback.

The Indians came next. Pharnazathres, son of Hydarnes, rode at their head. They wore armour of quilted cotton, and had bows of cane and bamboo arrows tipped with iron.

The Arians followed them. Sisamnes, son of Hydarnes, led them on horseback. Then came the Parthians and the Chorasmians. Artabazus, son of Pharnaces, rode at their head. After them marched the Sogdians. Azanes, son of Artæus, led them on horseback. Artyphius, son of Artabanus, Xerxes' nephew, led the Gandarians and the Dadicæ.

There were succeeded by the Caspians, clad in goatskins. Broad of figure and tanned by the sun, they peered from their hairy coverings. Ariomardus, son of Artyphius, led them on horseback. The Sarangæ followed in bizarrely colourful garments; buskins reaching to their knees gave them a martial air. Pherendates, son of Megabazus, rode at their head.

The Pactyes came after them, garbed in the skins of wild beasts. Artyntes, son of Ithamatres, led them on horseback.

Utians and Mycians followed. Arsamenes, son of Darius, Xerxes' stepbrother, rode at their head. Siromitres, son of Æobazus, rode before the Paricanians.

Then came the Arabs in long kilted coats, carrying bows that could be bent backward as well as forward. Next, the African Ethiopians. They were savage-looking figures in their lion and leopard skins, with their palmwood bows, four cubits long, and their long cane arrows tipped with the hard stone used to engrave seals. Besides, they had javelins headed with antelope horns ground to a point, and knotted clubs. Half their body was smeared with chalk, the other half with red ochre. Half white, half blood-red, with their black, kinky heads, they were repulsively horrible. Yet they were invincibly brave. Arsames, son of Darius and of Artystone, Xerxes' stepbrother, rode at their head.

The Indian Ethiopians followed. They were straight-haired. They wore the skins of horses' heads turned into helmets, with ears erect and flowing manes for crests. Their shields were made of the feathered skins of cranes. Who was their leader . . .?

Massages, son of Oarizus, rode at the head of the Libyans, black giants in untanned pelts.

Next came the Paphlagonians. They wore leather helmets from which projected their plaited hair-tufts. Their boots came to the middle of the leg. The Cappadocians, like them, were armed with bows and arrows. Dotus, son of Megasidrus, led the Paphlagonians on horseback, and Gobryas, son of Darius and Artystone, rode at the head of the Cappadocians.

The Phrygians followed with their conical caps, tops tilted forward. Then came the Armenians, colonists of the Phrygians. Xerxes' son-in-law, the youthful general Artochmes, led them on horseback.

The Lydians came next and after them the Mysians, bearing small, firm shields of rawhide and spears hardened by fire. Artaphrenes, son of that Artaphrenes who had commanded the Persians at Marathon, rode at their head.

The Asiatic Thracians, now known as Bithynians, followed. They wore foxskin helmets and voluminous, multi-coloured cloaks over their jerkins. Their buskins were of fawnskin. Bassaces, son of Artabanus and Xerxes' nephew, led them on horseback.

After them came the Chalybians, with brazen helmets in the shape of oxheads, shields of untanned oxhide, two lances to a man, and scarlet leggings on their calves. They were succeeded by the Cabalians, also known as Meïonians or Lasonians. Badres, son of Hystanes, led this innumerable horde.

The Moschians, wearing wooden helmets, followed. Ariomardus, son of Darius and of Parmys, rode at their head. The Mares came next and the Colchians. Pherendates, Teaspes' son, led them on horseback. The natives of the Erythræan islands succeeded. And which peoples came after them . . .?

The seconds in command rode at the head of corps of ten thousands, again subdivided into thousands and into hundreds.

A dazzling glitter in the sunlight. It is Mardonius, Xerxes' nephew and son-in-law, commander of all the hosts, with his staff: Tritantæchmes, son of Artabanus, Xerxes' nephew; Smerdomenes, son of Otanes, the queen's brother; then Masistes, Xerxes' brother, the son of Darius and of Atossa; Gergis, son of Arizus; Megabyzus, son of Zophyrus,—all on horseback surrounding Mardonius.

And now, after all the nations have marched thunderously across the plain of Doriscus and wheeled past Xerxes' throne, to face front in a line three deep, Mardonius with his staff rides up in blinding radiance. With him come the ten thousand Immortals, those famed invincibles, those picked giants, those magnificent statues of flesh and blood, shining in golden helmets and golden armour, bearing shields of gold and riding gold-bridled Nisæan horses. They ride on swaggering in sheer radiance, arrogance and vainglory while—rumbling and thundering—a rhythmically regulated roar of jubilation rises unanimously from all the soldiers of the host as Mardonius draws near.

He dismounts and advances to the throne, where Xerxes, gracefully embracing him, bids him sit by his side and watch the passing by of the cavalry.

First come the Sagartians, nomad horsemen, who thunder across the plain like a storm on small, swift, wild horses. They all carry nets and lassos. They whirl their lassos and snare the foeman they have marked. Then, yelling, they fling their net of twisted leather over him, and either kill him or capture him in a half-throttled condition. With shrill shouts, in a mad gallop, they dash by like a whirlwind.

The Indian cavalry races past in a frenzy. It rattles deafeningly along in chariots holding armed men and drawn by striped zebras.

Next, at a trot, the Cissians, Medes, Bactrians, Caspians, Libyans and Paricanians come on, all on mailed steeds, and with war chariots equipped with scythes that mow down all before them. They are followed by the Arabs, on fleet-footed camels.

Not counting camel-riders and war chariots, there are eighty thousand horsemen. They dash by in squadrons, in a furious equestrian dance. And each fantasia, according to race, differs in its brandishing of weapons, its flourishing of mantles and its cry of

[81]

homage addressed to the king. The Arabs on their
camels ride last lest the horses shy at their mounts.
No horse can endure seeing a camel. The two sons
of Datis—who commanded the Persians at Marathon, together with Artaphrenes—Armamithres and
Tithæus, waving their swords, ride at the head of
the cavalry.

The march past has lasted for hours. Yet Xerxes
does not tire. He never wearies of the spectacle of
his power. Now that the generals and the captains
have aligned their masses of soldiers—never yet has
so gigantically numerous a host been seen—in order
of battle on the plain, Xerxes mounts his war chariot. Mardonius rides beside him. Round about
him ride the Immortals. He seems a sun of golden
radiance with rays of gold, moving across the plain.

Xerxes inspects all with amiability and condescension. With his self-satisfied smile he talks of his
countless brothers, nephews and sons-in-law, and
asks numerous questions. Beside his chariot scribes
importantly set down questions and answers in
cuneiform script on long rolls of papyrus. The sun
burns down upon the army drawn up in battle array
all day long; yet Xerxes, the Sun on earth, does not
tire. After he has finished inspecting the footmen
and the horsemen, he has himself conducted to the
strand. The sun beats searingly on the sea, and on
the fleet stretching beyond reach of eye. From the
shore the fleet at sea is as far beyond the range of
vision as is the army in the plain, and this very
duality of the immeasurable fills Xerxes with satisfaction.

He enters his Sidonian galley of state—it is very
long—and seats himself under a baldachin of cloth
of gold. In that burning sun, on those waves mir-

roring a golden sheen, the vessel, the king and all those surrounding him seem one mass of radiant gold. The savage soldiery on the shore regard the spectacle without knowing what to make of it. It is not hard for them to believe Xerxes a god, at the very least a son of Ormuzd, Mithra, perhaps. Xerxes' galley moves along the prows of the aligned ships lying at anchor. They are four plethra off from shore. Their bows point upward in a challenging curve, facing the land. Their garrisons of marines are marshalled on deck in battle array. The king passes slowly along the line of prows.

Yonder lie the Phœnicians and Syrians with three hundred triremes. Their marines wear impenetrable linen corselets, as tough as leather, and they are armed in the Greek manner.

The Egyptians have two hundred triremes. The men wear helmets of woven reeds, ringed with iron bands. Huge swords and long, broad shields make them formidable fighting men.

The Cyprians number a hundred fifty triremes. They look so very Greek that Xerxes is vaguely surprised.

The Cilicians occupy a hundred triremes. Their shields of untanned oxhide, with the hair turned outward, make a strange impression. They look like a herd of oxen with helmeted human heads.

The Pamphylians lie at anchor with thirty triremes. And they, too, look much like Greeks.

The Lycians have fifty triremes. The marines are armoured, their calves protected by *knemides*, brazen greaves. Goatskin mantles hang from their shoulders, and on their heads are winged caps. They carry poniards and long scythes.

The Asiatic Dorians fill thirty ships, and once

more Xerxes frowns because of their Hellenic aspect. On the other hand, the Carians, lying at anchor with seventy vessels, please him because of the murderous scythes they use as weapons.

There lie the Ionians with a hundred ships. They look very Greek. Might the Ionians . . .?

The Islanders lie at anchor with no more than sixteen vessels, but the Æolians have sixty. Persians, Medes and Sacæ are distributed among the vessels. The Phœnician are the best, especially the long ships of Sidon.

Xerxes passes by the flagship. Among the numerous admirals of fleets are Ariabignes and Achæmenes, sons of Darius and Xerxes' brothers; Megabazus, son of Megabetes; Prexaspes, son of Aspiathes. Round about them, in rank and file, are all the other captains of the fleet, with their magnificently sonorous names, names Sidonian, Tyrian and Persian that ring like chime of gong and clash of cymbal.— Tetramnestus, son of Anysus, Syennesis, son of Oromedon, Cybernisus, son of Sicas, Timonax, son of Timagoras, Damasithymos, son of Candaules.

Against Xerxes' appreciative ears, as he is oared past and scans the cheering captains of the fleet with encouraging and condescending glances, crash these splendidly ringing names which a secretary repeats to him. The secretary is well instructed and has a voice like a herald.

As they pass the flagship someone in the king's suite calls out in a ringing voice:

"Artemisia, daughter of Lygdamis, Queen-Regent of Halicarnassus!"

The queen lies at anchor with five magnificently equipped triremes; the ships of Sidon alone can compare with them. She governs in the name of her son, still a child. A daring Amazon, she has not hesitated to follow Xerxes to battle, at sea. There stands her helmed figure, her black hair flowing down like a mane over her golden corselet, cheering the King of Kings together with her people, the men of Halicarnassus, of Cos and of Nisyrus. Xerxes smiles at her with great courtesy and grace, and in the most amiable manner.

The king passes along the line of the transports which are to bring across the horses, zebras and camels, the war chariots and the provisions.

Xerxes turns. He sees—not the harbour, which is too small—but the very border of the ocean, fenced in for miles by his tremendous fleet. The profiles of the high spurred rams and broad fighting beaks merge in each other in an endless successive line. The masts merge endlessly in each other like a winged forest. The sails, unfurled for this gala occasion, multi-coloured, only gently stirred by the breeze, merge into each other in a succession of yellow, scarlet, green, violet, indigo-blue and white spots.

Far, far away on the Doriscan plain the distant, vaguely shining squares of the soldiery, burned by the sunlight, merge into one another. To the horizon's farthest reaches nothing is visible save Xerxes' host and his fleet.

He smiles, and the arrogance bred of his power makes him feel himself a superman.

## CHAPTER XIII

## DEMARETUS

THAT night Xerxes was unable to sleep. It was the first night that he lay sleepless. To the amazement of his bodyguards whose duty it was to follow him at a prescribed distance, Xerxes left his bed-chamber in the palace of Doriscus and stepped out upon the great terrace whose lofty battlements afforded a view of the plain and the far-flung sea.

It was a night in early summer, the heavens powdered with the diamond dust of countless stars. On the broad, nocturnal plain the shimmering, teeming lines of tents were barely distinguishable as they stretched far, far into the distance, like a dike losing itself in darkness. On the broad sea, scarce visible behind the outlines of the ships' keels blotting out each other, rose the spindling forest of masts whose sails for the nonce were furled. A radiant mist floated over everything. Xerxes looked about him, seated himself on a throne—there was a throne on the terrace, for Xerxes found thrones provided wherever he went—and called out to the captain of his guard who had followed him to the terrace entrance: "I would have King Demaretus attend me."

The command rang out superbly on the silent, immeasurable night. With that indeterminate vision —which yet was real—of his army round about him and of his fleet before him on the sea, only a King of Kings, only a Xerxes, because he had insomnia, could send for the King Demaretus to wait on him in the middle of the night. It is true that Xerxes had to wait a bit. While he was waiting he watched falling stars shoot down from the skies like arrows. Yet not long did he wait. For King Demaretus soon put in an appearance, trying hard not to look sleepy.

Demaretus had been King of Sparta, but as a result of various intrigues he had fled to Darius, who had honourably provided for him at his court. He was much esteemed by the Persians, and had accompanied Xerxes, though he refused to fight against his own people and his Greek blood-brethren.

With a careless gesture, Xerxes said:

"Be seated, Demaretus."

He forgot, however, that his throne was the only seat available, so that Demaretus, after gazing helplessly about him, with a composure developed by

[87]

experience sat down at Xerxes' feet. It was an intimate scene: the night, nightgowns and, covering them more or less adequately, royal robes.

"I have been wanting to speak to you," Xerxes began. "I hardly had a glimpse of you today, because of the review. Where were you?"

"In your suite, Great King, behind you," said Demaretus.

"Ah, and so you were," replied Xerxes. "But I want to speak to you now, for I cannot sleep. Do you sleep well?"

"That's as may be, Majesty."

"Do you ever have nightmares? Do you often dream dreams? Your mother dreamt a great deal, didn't she? And are you yourself not the child of a dream?"

"My mother, whom many have accused of sleeping with a muleteer," said Demaretus somewhat dryly, "did, in fact, give birth to me after she had dreamt of the hero Astrobacus. If I be not the son of Sparta's king, Ariston—I myself doubt it, because his wife bore me in advance of her term—then I am the son of the shade of the said hero Astrobacus, of whom my mother dreamt."

"That is a strange tale," absent-mindedly remarked Xerxes, as he excitedly rubbed his forehead. "I, too, often dream strange dreams, and so does my uncle Artabanus. I dreamt it was the will of the gods that I declare war on Greece. Tell me honestly, Demaretus, what is your opinion? Can you really for a single moment think or imagine that the Greeks and the Western peoples, between whom there exists such a lack of unity and co-operation, would have a chance . . . that is, could resist my attacks?"

"O King!" said Demaretus. "Is it your wish that

here, in the silence of night, while our glances range over your army and your fleet, I pour sweet words of flattery into your ear?"

"Tell me the truth, Demaretus!"

"Then speak I shall, Majesty," replied Demaretus. "Never will the Greeks come to offer you water and earth. Never will the Greeks listen to your proposals."

"Will they truly not?"

"On the contrary, they will march out to meet you."

"Do you mean what you say?"

"They will offer you battle."

"All the Greeks?"

"The Lacedæmonians, my own people, will surely do so, even were the others to submit to you."

"Are the Lacedæmonians numerous?"

"Do not ask me how many they number, O King! If they be but a thousand strong they will defeat you. If there be no more than three hundred of them they will, nevertheless, attack you and rob you of your victory."

Xerxes broke into irritated laughter.

"Demaretus! Would you fight ten Persians, or rather twenty? For you are a king, and a Spartan king can take on a double quota of men, can't he? Demaretus, let me tell you something. If the Greeks and your Lacedæmonians all resemble you, the seaman's child and the son of a dream, if not of a muleteer, then I fear your words are but idle boasts. I have already seen other Greeks and other Lacedæmonians. They never made much of an impression on me. Besides, they have no armies, no monarchs. Have you seen the Immortals, whose sovereign I am? Have you noticed those torsos of theirs? One

of them can get the better of three Lacedæmonians—
especially if his sergeant is standing behind him, lash
in hand. No! Not even if they were our equals in
number, for— Look at my army, look at my fleet!"

With a grandiloquent gesture Xerxes indicated
his limitlessness, shining silver-bright in the starlight.

"Majesty!" said Demaretus calmly, "you are not
pleased to hear the truth. Yet the Spartans are as I
have described them. I must do them justice, though
they have given me much cause for complaint. They
have not respected my privileges, they have slan-
dered my mother, they have made me an outlaw and
a proscript. Your father Darius—"

"Yes, my never-to-be-forgotten father!" cried
Xerxes excitedly, and thought of his parent's unfor-
tunate campaign against Hellas.

"Your never-to-be-forgotten father," Demaretus
corrected himself, "received me graciously. He gave
me a palace and a Persian princess for wife, and he
gave me the cities of Pergamus, Teuthrania and
Halisarne. Do I not owe him and his son a debt of
gratitude? . . . No, I cannot do battle with ten
men. Yet, if needs must, I would take on one of
your Immortals. And this holds good of all Spartans. Man to man they are inferior to none, united
they are unconquerable."

Xerxes shrugged his shoulders.

"Whom do they obey?" he asked.

"The law," replied Demaretus.

"The law?" queried Xerxes, in surprise.

"The law," repeated Demaretus, "which forbids
them to flee."

Xerxes burst into loud, hysterical laughter.

Then he rose and drew Demaretus to him by the

sleeve. Together they walked to the end of the terrace. Xerxes gazed into the distance, before and around him. Again his hand made a grandiloquent gesture.

"It is impossible," said he, and thus silenced his own fears.

"Majesty, may all be according to your wish," spoke Demaretus.

Slowly Xerxes walked back and into the palace, without again looking at Demaretus.

And that was the first of Xerxes' sleepless nights.

## CHAPTER XIV

## ACANTHUS

**X**ERXES' army resembled a torrent in spate, that carries along with it all waters it encounters. When Xerxes left Doriscus he ordered all the Thracian peoples—they had been subject to him ever since Mardonius had made them Persian vassals before Marathon—to march to war with him. They obeyed. When the soldiers were between the towns of Mesambria and Stryme, divided by the river Lissus, they drank the Lissus dry.

Mardonius and Masistes led a third of the host along the shore of the sea. Tritantæchmes and

Gergis conducted a second third farther back, through the interior. The remainder followed, with Xerxes in their midst.

Desolate and ravaged countries were left in their wake, just as their path was marked by dry river beds. The lakes of Ismaris and Bistonis near Dicæa were hardly sufficient to quench their thirst. The river Nestus was like a swallow of water in the hands they raised to drink, and a brackish sea, measuring thirty stadia in circumference, was little more than a troughful for the mules of the train. The Pætians, the Ciconians, the Bistonians, the Sapæi, the Dersæi and the Edoni were compelled—since it seemed to offer the only chance for existence—to follow the armies of the King of Kings. Or, perhaps, since their cattle had also been carried off they did so only because they wished to leave the cities and fields which the hosts had eaten empty and cleared of grain. These peoples followed on land and at sea, together with their women, children and all their possessions. Only the Satræ refused to join them. These were wild Thracians, never yet subdued, who from their heights, always covered with dense forest and white with snow in the winter, laughed scornfully at Xerxes' host.

The torrent in spate streamed steadily westward. When Xerxes reached the Strymon the Magians sacrificed snow-white steeds on the bank of the stream. They were slaughtered ritually, in a pit. For the blood of the victim may not defile the pure water. The Magians laid the sacrifices on a bed of myrtle and laurel boughs and burned them, digging about meanwhile in the fire with their slender rods and pouring milk and honey round about on the earth. And while they sacrificed and poured libation they sang their sacrificial hymns. The entrails of the horses promised good fortune.

The Strymon, a broad river, was not drunk dry. It was crossed by countless bridges over which the soldiers marched. On the opposite side the country was known as the Field of the Nine Roads. There the Magians again offered sacrifice, so that the alien gods might look favourably upon the king's campaign. Nine youths and nine maidens were chosen from among the natives and there burned alive to honour the deities of the underworld.

In Acanthus Xerxes took a somewhat longer rest, and there he had the satisfaction of learning that the canal through Mount Athos had been completed. Yet he was deeply grieved at hearing that Artachæus, the Achæmenian giant who measured five royal cubits less four fingers in height and whose voice inspired terror, was no more. While superintending with Bubares the work of boring and splitting he had died of a malignant intestinal complaint. "It is a misfortune for all Persia," said Xerxes and ordered fleet and army to go into particularly deep mourning.

And Xerxes bade the Acanthians erect a stone monument on Artachæus' grave and to offer sacrifices to him as to a demigod. This they did, and together with the professional mourners, they apostrophized the dead man with loud cries:

"Artachæus! Artachæus!"

During Xerxes' stay in Acanthus the maintenance of his table impoverished all the wealthy Acanthians. In despair they sought out Antipatrus, son of Orgus, the richest among the Thracians, who had entertained the king in Thasus. "Antipatrus!" cried the wealthy Acanthians, who had well-nigh been re-

duced to beggary, to the great man of Thasus now
become a captain of Xerxes' host. "Antipatrus!"
they cried to him in the market-place. "We appeal to
you! What was the cost of the banquet you offered
Xerxes in Thasus?"

"It came to at least four hundred talents of silver,"
said Antipatrus calmly. The banquet was one that
had been offered the king in the name of the city of
Thasus, on the mainland. "And I really think it
filled the bill," Antipatrus added modestly.

The wretched, practically beggared Acanthians
flung up their arms in despair.

"Four hundred talents of silver!" they clamoured
in a confusion of voices. "That is why the King
of Kings is not content here. Yet we do all that we
can. But we have to set the royal table every day,
Antipatrus, to say nothing of the army and the
fleet."

Megacreon of Abdera, who had been obliged to
follow the army from that city, drew nearer. He
remarked: "Worthy Acanthians! You might better praise the gods that the King of Kings does not
dine at noon as he does at eve, and that he is satisfied
to eat but once a day."

The wealthy Acanthians piteously begged Antipatrus and Megacreon to follow them a little way,
to the market-place before the town.

There they showed what they had been doing for
months past, ever since the arrival of Xerxes' heralds demanding earth and water for their master.
Tremendous millstones, uninterruptedly turned by
asses and slaves, were grinding corn. Cattle of the
finest had been rounded up and penned. There
were great corrals filled with beeves, other corrals
filled with sheep and goats. There were great arti-

ficial ponds for fish and water fowl. Tens of thousands of men, women and children were toiling there under superintendents. Goldsmiths and silversmiths were constantly busy making new vessels, and carpenters new seats and couches. For furniture as well as plate disappeared every night from the palace where Xerxes ate his evening meal.

The army lay outside the city. And the total of Xerxes' host as well as of his fleet, so it was said, had swollen to a mass of five million twenty-three thousand and two hundred men, owing to the field armies of Thrace which had been forced into the campaign.

Yet no one has ever computed the number of eunuchs, concubines, slaves and children who accompanied all these millions of generals, princes and warriors. And no one, after making a count of the horses, has ever enumerated the camels, zebras, pack animals and Indian dogs which were sent in advance or followed on behind. Since all these ate and drank as they passed by it is easy to understand why the beds of all the rivers lay exposed and the richest dwellers in the land were beggared after the army had gone.

And now Xerxes' host was about to invade Thessaly.

And Xerxes' fleet was to sail through the canal which divided Mount Athos.

## CHAPTER XV

## THE TWO CULTURES

IN HELLAS and Lacedæmonia the Athenians and Spartans awaited the menace approaching from the east. They realized that the coming struggle would be one to preserve their culture.

* * *

The Persian empire was not old. Young and as yet unworn, the Persians had vanquished ancient, devitalized Media under Cyrus, and Cyrus' daughter Atossa was the mother of Xerxes. Yet in the course of three generations a people, though not aged and exhausted as was the case with the Medes after the passing of many centuries, does change in body and in spirit, in blood and in soul. Cyrus, son of Cambyses the Persian and the Median princess Maridane, was already half a Mede, although he had inherited his half of young, Persian blood from his father. When Cyrus as a boy saw his grandfather Astyages, King of the Medes, whom he was later to overthrow, he noticed that the old man's eyes were painted and his face rouged, and that he wore a wig and a flowing Median gown. Cyrus thought his grandfather so handsome that when his mother Maridane asked him: "Which do you think the handsomer, your father Cambyses or your grandfather Astyages?" he answered: "I think my father the handsomest man among the Persians and my grandfather among the Medes."

And Cyrus thought so because his mother was a Mede. Later, when he had become a king and an invincible captain, he ordered the Persians to wear the flowing Median robe as their national dress and reproved none who rouged, not even his generals and admirals.

Yet the men of Hellas and of Lacedæmonia, the Athenians and the Spartans, never painted their faces.

Persian civilization was not old. It had merely attained its perfect maturity and was in its ripest bloom. It was magnificent wherever the building up and administration of the state were concerned. Just as Cyrus had founded the Royal Post, with its postmasters and trotting postmen with fresh relays of horses ever in readiness, throughout the Persian Empire, all else in that empire had been established with the same thoroughness. Administrative cohesion linked the imperial satrapies like a golden

[98]

girdle, and governance and the finances were properly divided and subdivided, as was the regulation of the army and the fleet. In the same way was prescribed which city should furnish the veils of the Persian queen and which her handkerchiefs. All was magnificent, indescribably magnificent in its order, and the Persian ideal was the domination of all other cultures, even those of the West.

The Greek civilization was young. Though as yet hardly aware of the fact, it held an altogether different ideal. This ideal of its youth was not omnipotent control of the existing material world; rather, it was based on the perfecting of the human spirit which was to dwell in a perfectly beautiful human body. During the four years Xerxes was preparing to win world dominion with his millions, stretching out his hand toward the West, Pindar was singing his odes in honour of the victors in the Olympian games, and Æschylus was thinking and writing his divine tragedies. Nothing is left of the bridge across the Hellespont, nor of the canal through Mount Athos. But ode and tragedy remain immortal, immortal according to all human standards.

Without as yet being fully aware of it, Athens already sensed within herself that which was to be: the age of Phidias and of Pericles.

But in Susa, the capital of Persia, in the palace of the King of Kings, the numerous queens, princesses and concubines surrounding Atossa never dreamed for a moment that the age of Cyrus was already past its bloom.

## CHAPTER XVI

## DELPHI SPEAKS

XERXES' heralds to demand earth and water had been sent neither to Athens nor to Sparta. For the heralds Darius had once dispatched for this purpose the Athenians and Lacedæmonians had flung into the pits destined for those condemned to death, with the insulting advice therein to seek earth and water for their king. Thereafter the entrails of the Spartan sacrificial victims had been particularly unfavourable, and the Lacedæmonians had sent Sperthias and Bulis, two of their most distinguished elders, to Xerxes at Susa to atone for the death of the Persian heralds. Xerxes in a wondrously magnanimous mood sent the two scapegoats back to Sparta.

He did not, as Darius had done, send heralds to Athens and Sparta, and in Hellas and Lacedæmonia the Greeks awaited the menacing danger approaching out of the East.

Aristonica, the Pythian priestess, sat in the sanctuary upon the sacred tripod. The vapours swirled around her. Facing her sat the envoys.

She stuttered:

"Unhappy wretches! Why do you sit here? Leave your homes and the rock of the Acropolis! Flee to the ends of the earth! Athens will be destroyed."

All the envoys had risen. But the Pythoness, carried away by the sacred frenzy, continued:

"Your city will be a prey to the flames, and Ares, the terrible god, riding a war chariot of the East, will destroy not alone your castles and towers, but those of other cities as well! Flames will devour your temples, that already run with sweat and tremble with terror, and the black blood is already dripping from your rooftops! Woe upon you, ye Athenians! Leave my sanctuary and arm yourselves with courage to withstand so great a calamity!"

The envoys rushed out of the temple and gazed up at its gabled roof. Yet no blood was dripping from it. Therefore they ventured to return the following day, yet now coming humbly, as petitioners, with olive branches in their hands, to question Apollo's oracle.

Kneeling in a circle about the Pythoness, they prayed:

"Phœbus Apollo! Grant us a more favourable answer, now that we kneel humbly before you, bearing these olive branches! Else we will remain here on our knees until we have breathed our last."

Then, in broken gasps, the voice of Aristonica sounded from out the vaporous clouds of incense:

"In vain Pallas Athene stands before her father Zeus and implores him to save her city. Nothing can move him. Hear, ye Athenians, his final irrevocable decision! When the enemy shall have taken possession of all the land of Cecrops and the sacred Cithæron, Zeus grants his daughter and her city a wall of wood. Leave your city, Athenians, and protect yourselves with a wooden wall!"

"A wooden wall?" The kneeling envoys reflected.

"And you, divine Salamis," continued the oracle, "shall cause the sons of women to perish! You shall cause them to perish, I repeat, whether Demeter is scattered or gathered in!"

The envoys returned to Athens.

## CHAPTER XVII

## THEMISTOCLES

IN ATHENS the Attic genius was ripening. Even though not the genius of perfected wisdom, even though not the genius of perfected art, nevertheless, the genius of Hellenic humanity was already ripening. This humanity was not as yet—as it was later, in science and art—to rival the divine. Yet for all it remained within human bounds, it blossomed forth into genius.

It revealed itself in Themistocles. All those qualities, delicate and strong, joyous and serious, cunning and emotional, statesmanlike and martial, which could come to fruition at one and the same

time in the genial soul of a mortal born in the southland were united in Themistocles, orator and warrior. To oppose him Persia could produce only
the imposing arrogance of her tremendous strength,
only the blind obedience—even that of its countless
princes—which the well-ordered compulsion a supreme autocracy secured.

Themistocles, son of Neocles, in the days of his
first flaming youth had been an ostentatious wastrel
and night-hawk whom his father had disowned.
Yet while still barely more than a boy he had
fought beside Miltiades at Marathon, and there had
amply atoned for his earlier irresponsibility. The
lost son had regained his fatherland, and such a gain
was a precious achievement. For in those days love
of one's natal land was more than mere sentiment
and a sense of security. Love of one's land was
synonymous with virtue. In Athens love for the
Attic fatherland even excluded love for Sparta.
Since then patriotic affection has gradually gained
a broader vision, and will continue to develop until
it embraces the world at large. At that time the
Athenian knew but a single virtue, to love Athens
not alone better than Persia, but better than Sparta,
and to help Athens gain the hegemony over all the
states of Greece, even over Sparta.

Themistocles, whose type of genius was com-
pounded of many contradictory qualities, nursed his
ambition while he indulged himself with the smiling indifference of the man of pleasure. Yet his
ambition was the stronger. All that was frivolous
had to take second place. The air of Hellas was
that of youth. The virtues, which in themselves
comprised all simple, unpretentious beauty, blossomed there like thrifty fruit-trees in a luxuriant

[104]

garden, throttling the tares. Hellas, still burgeoning into blossom, became an altogether different world from Persia, already in its fulness of bloom. Themistocles often said that the laurels of Miltiades—who had beaten the Persians at Marathon, for all that Xerxes did not admit that this was historically true—would give him insomnia. This insomnia of Themistocles differed from that of Xerxes.

When the *theoroi* returned to Athens, the Pythoness' speech soon made the rounds. A wooden wall! A wooden wall! An excited dread, which turned to despair, filled every soul. Then Themistocles addressed the Athenians. A novel note sounded in his voice, and rang radiantly out upon this young world where the germs of things new and unborn floated in the sultry, ripening atmosphere.

"Athenians! Why ask your wise men and priests to tell you what is meant by the wooden wall mentioned by the venerated Pythoness? Do you think for a moment that the rotten wooden palisade still encircling our Acropolis can protect us from the tremendous danger come out of the East, and the Persian sea that threatens us with its deluge? Why this terrible fear, turning to despair? Does the Pythoness foretell our own or the enemy's misfortune? Would she have mentioned Salamis the blessed if the sons who are destined to fall were our own? Would she not rather have called Salamis the accursed? No, ye Athenians! The wooden wall that is meant is the wall of our ships!"

The new note rang out powerfully above the anxious warnings of the prophets of evil: that it would be better to leave Attica and flee elsewhere—

yet where? The new note was not only martial, seriously moving, joyous and strong as though sounded by a young god; it was subtle and politically sound as well. It not only sounded enthusiastic, it was practically convincing. Following Themistocles' advice the gold and silver in the state treasury, the ingots from the mines of Laurion—equally divided among all citizens come of age, each would have received ten drachmæ—had been spent on a fleet to fight the Æginetæ. The ships, already built, but which had not yet been used for their intended purpose, lay untouched in the harbour.

"Is not our fleet already at hand?" The new note rang out like a cock's crow in the golden dawn.

The young sea power had been created.

## CHAPTER XVIII

## HURRICANE OFF PELION

WHILE the King of Kings, with a host that kept increasing as it marched, passed through Thessaly, the enormous Persian fleet sailed along the coast of Magnesia, and came to anchor between the city of Casthanæa and the coast of Sepias. There was not a single harbour. The foremost line of ships edged the beach with its prows. The others came to anchor behind them, till all the hundreds of vessels were riding at anchor, behind each other, in eight rows. In the last rows the anchors already plunged so many fathoms that the crews were alarmed. The night was dark and threatening. A cold wind blew. It seemed as though Boreas, who had wedded an Athenian maid, Orithyia, daughter of Erechtheus, were threatening the Persian fleet with one of his northers. Had not an oracle foretold that Athens might count upon the aid of her son-in-law? And was not Boreas, the North Wind, her son-in-law? And that night Athens' son-in-law blew about the Persian keels till they shook on the waves and danced against each other. The Ægean Sea lay broad and black beneath a sable nocturnal sky, piling up huge billows. Toward morning a heavy storm suddenly arose. "It is the Hellespontine gale!" cried the coast dwellers, who came to bring food for the sailors, busy disentangling their crossed cables. In the twinkling of an eye the gale turned into a raging tempest. In spite of the dawn it continued night, and the hurricane piled the billows higher and higher, and flung and smashed the triremes one against the other. The crews of the first line of ships drew their vessels up on the shore, where they lay as though stranded, yet safe from the greatest danger. Yet the ships on the open sea, over which Boreas ranged, he tore from their anchors and cast against each other. Furiously he demolished them, or, with a sky-high toss of giant waves, blew them against the rocks and riffles of Mount Pelion, which raised its gigantic buckler on the water's edge like some long, steep wall of fate. The despairing ships were scattered and wrecked as far as Casthanæa, as far as Meliboia.

For three days and nights the catastrophe ran its course. On the fourth day, when the summer seas were again blue and smiling, more than four hundred vessels washed their wreckage, broken spars, tatters of sail and the corpses of their crews, up on shore. On the foreland of Sepias a Magnesian, Aminocles, son of Cretinus, dwelt on a large estate which stretched from the mountains down to the rocky strand. While he, with all his people, was mourning the death of his sons, who had perished in the storm, the appeased waves mockingly rolled one golden goblet after another, rolled all the silver cups, which had not yet sunk, to his feet. In one and the same day the gods tore from him all his offspring and enriched him with Persian treasure. He knew not whether to laugh or weep.

The Magians now sacrificed to the Winds, to Thetis and to the Nereids. But the sea already had quieted without these sacrifices. And yet the most useless things men think they must do, especially things to propitiate the gods, are of supreme beauty, the beauty of gesture and of thought.

Xerxes did not at once hear about the catastrophe. Together with his armies he had passed through Thessaly to the Mælian Gulf. His host now numbered approximately six million men. Everywhere the land was eaten bare, the rivers drunk dry. It seemed as though Xerxes had grown during these days. His figure was taller and he looked more regal than ever before. His continually straying glance, however, betrayed a curious restlessness, and since his review at Doriscus he had not slept well. On the shore of the Mælian Gulf the tide ebbs and flows several times a day, and Xerxes would stare at the flood-tide and the ebb-tide when the one approached his feet and the other withdrew from them across the moist, grooved sand. He meditated and —when he had but just fallen asleep—he dreamed of the outgoing and incoming tides.

And now, circling the Mælian Gulf, he had

reached the plain of Trachis. He was fascinated by
this countryside, since it abounded with recollections
of Hercules, son of Zeus, and Hellas' great hero.
There, back of the town of Trachis, the erstwhile
Heraclæia, Mount Œta stretched into the white
clouds of the blue heavens, the Œta on whose peak
Hercules had rendered up his soul to the gods on
the funeral pyre. It is most fascinating here, thought
Xerxes, while he gazed about him. Between the
rivers Melas and Æsopus, over the vast breadth of
the plain, within sight of the sea, spread the tented
macrocosm of his hosts.

Xerxes debated with his generals as to how he
might penetrate farther into Hellas. For the mountains to which he raised his eyes seemed an impass-
able wall. It was then that Ephialtes, the traitor,
was led into his presence.

## CHAPTER XIX

## THERMOPYLÆ

IN THE meantime the allied Hellenes guarded Thermopylæ. They were hardly more than five thousand in number.

It was a narrow pass, the only road along which it was possible to enter Hellas. At Anthela it was barely possible for a single broad, ox-drawn cart to drive through the cleft in the rock. At Alpenos the same cart could just pass out. The walls of rock rise perpendicularly on the one side, and on the other the sea shimmers and shines in deep lagoons above the abysses of gorges lying far below the surface of the water.

[111]

Holm-oaks, with their black boles and fantastic limbs, tower knottedly amid the rocks, and the sea looks even more blue when glimpsed between the green-black verdure of the ancient trees. Still bluer are the *chytroi*, the women's baths, the warm pools, blue with a blue unknown to any other waters. There rises an altar dedicated to Hercules, the hero of that place. Ponderous old gates of wood and bronze bar access to it. And there a high wall lifts itself up where the rocks contract. The awe of olden, mythical days at most times weights this loneliness and silence. The baths are no longer used, the gates are in ruins. The altar, however, is still served. Now and again an eagle floats on broad pinions over the seemingly enchanted landscape, followed by another. Owing to the harmonious colouring of the blue sea and blue pools, the grey rocks and gorges, the nearly black verdure of the holm-oaks, and to their contrast with each other, the spot takes on a kind of divine beauty. Wherever the gods—and the demigods as well—set foot, they left beauty in their wake. Not only Hercules' tragic sorrow echoes here, but his laughter as well, so profoundly bass and yet so clear. It rang out at the Melampygian Rock, where he tied together the two sons of Thela, the Nereid, who mocked every passer-by, and swung them across his shoulders, under his lion-skin. Their mother had often warned them not to make a mock of passers-by, lest the Bogieman with the black-haired behind get them. Suddenly the two rascals laughed loudly, and Hercules asked how it came that, though bound and hanging downward across his shoulders, they were laughing so loudly. So they told him, and admitted that their mother's prophecy had at last been fulfilled. For Hercules was very hairy. Thereupon the hero laughed even more loudly than the rascals themselves and turned them loose.

When the wind blew about the rock it seemed to wake an echo of that laughter of immemorial days. Yet farther up the landscape grew sterner, the rocks more sacred, the sea more divine, as though this spot were destined to greatness in advance, and as though for that reason it was guarded by a few thousand Hellenes, who had gathered around Leonidas.

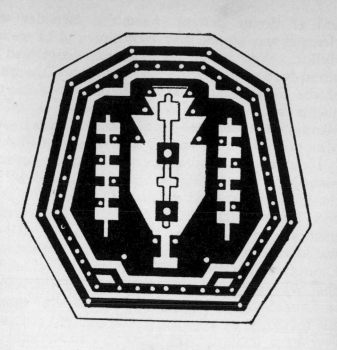

## CHAPTER XX

## LEONIDAS

LEONIDAS! There is a man on whom History has been unable to lavish her irony. Irony never has touched him, and in the major beauty of the youthful, simple world of blossoming Hellas he was the hero, the model of heroes, almost a demigod among mortals. Around Leonidas history is transfigured into myth. Leonidas! In reality he was not other than history has transmitted him to us. He was young, noble, blond and King of Sparta. He was a descendant of Hercules and of the latter's son Hyllos. In his blond athletic beauty this king, who was a hero and of divine descent, resembled Hercules when Hercules was young, and even more did he resemble Hyllos. Yet above all, Leonidas resembled the blond hero of all the myths: Meleagros, the hunter of the Calydonian boar; Bellerophontes, the conqueror of Pegasus; Perseus, who struck off the Medusa's snake-filleted head; Theseus, who slew the Minotaur; Jason, who gained the Golden Fleece.

He alone was descended from Hercules, yet in his beauty the blond King of Sparta compared with all the greatest heroes of myth. There was no difference between them. In him myth has remained history, and history has turned to myth. All that was divine in simple humanity was transposed in Leonidas from dream-thought to reality, and all that was human in loftiest divinity has developed, in Leonidas, into a tangible historic ideal that has the loveliness of an antique statue. No poet could ever have imagined for himself a handsomer hero than Leonidas, King of Sparta.

In History which, face to face with him, is devoid of irony, he remains the model of all heroes. He shines with the radiance of a marble image in the dawn-glow of his fame. History smiles at Xerxes. Xerxes has been booked in History's ironic annals. But History has never smiled at Leonidas. When his name is spoken History raises her maternal countenance, proudly and gratefully, that face with the features of a goddess who cannot be softened, and from her divine eyes well two long, pearly tears.

Leonidas! Who among us, in boyhood days, has not beheld him in his beauty, when his melodious name first rang in our ears, when for the first time his marble image rose transcendent before us? He has the glory of our years of youth. He compelled our adolescent student admiration like none other.

It may have been because he was so divinely beautiful, so fabulously blond, so athletically handsome, and at the same time golden fair, as radiant as a sungod between the rocky walls of Thermopylæ, casting their menacing shadows, and because he vanished in those very shadows—as a sun-god always vanishes in night, once his heroic task is done.

In my love for authenticity I have identified Leonidas, that blond King of the Sparta of an already tangibly historic day, with the Homeric heroes of the half-mythic, half-historic times of ancient Ilium. Leonidas! I have loved him better than Achilles, whom I love, nevertheless, and no less than Hector, whom I love more than Achilles. Leonidas! I still hold him in affection, and now that I am writing about him with the often ironic annals of History at hand, I shall never smile at him as at Xerxes, but only speak his name with admiration and love, and stretch out to him a final laurel branch.

Leonidas!

## CHAPTER XXI

## THE RIDER ON THE HILLSIDE

THAT morning Xerxes sent a horseman up the high rocks to spy out the mysterious gateway to the warm baths. The horseman, on guard at the right and the left against any possible danger in that wilderness, let his horse climb amid holm-oaks and brush, slowly ascending the rocky masses. The Persians are great horsemen. This Immortal was a wonderful horseman, and his horse knew where to set its hoofs. Xerxes stared from below, from his throne—carried after him, everywhere—up at the scout. The latter stood out clearly against the blue sky like some radiant equestrian statue of gold and bronze.  At last Xerxes noticed that the horseman was riding carefully along the ridge of the mountain, despite the danger of falling into the abyss.

The rider on the height, who stood out so radiantly against the blue sky—he may have been within reach of a Lacedæmonian arrow—was looking down.  He was very much surprised.  He could not believe his eyes.  The entire pass through the mountain was deserted.  Only yonder, where the breadth between the rocks was greatest, a few white tent-pickets, scarce higher than the rest, showed over a more elevated tent.  About a thousand other tent-tops were grouped about this higher tent.  Before it, on a boulder, sat a man in the position of Achilles when he sat before his tent.  One leg was crossed over the other, and his chin was resting on his palm.  There he sat, meditatively, his head bent down.  That helmed head was blond.  Thick, curly hair fell sunnily golden about the broad bare neck, which emerged from the brightly shining gorget of his armour.  Nobly athletic, the heroic muscles of his youthfully regal manliness stood out on the half-bared arms and legs.

That must be Leonidas, thought the Persian horseman, Leonidas, King of Sparta, descendant of Hellas' greatest hero, Hercules, the Leonidas of whom the men of the Persian army had already heard.

The horseman looked down upon Leonidas with the greatest surprise.  The King of Sparta did not sit upon a throne like the King of Kings.  He sat on a boulder.  No bodyguard of Immortals and no staff of generals, brothers-in-law, brothers and nephews surrounded him.  Very simply the King of Sparta sat there and seemed to be thinking. His chin was resting in his hand, and one knee rested powerfully and easily upon the other. The Persian horseman would never have imagined he was a king, not even a king of Sparta.

Yet when the Persian's glances strayed farther afield he was still more surprised. Below, in that cleft, were no more than some four thousand men. They were scattered along the long gorge and seemed to be in good spirits. Some practised throwing their spears. Others cast the quoit, and again others were running races. The merry laughter of the victor in an athletic game rang out loudly and boyishly. Yet what surprised the Persian most of all was that the majority of these men down below were smoothing their hair—which fell in curls to their necks—as though they were adorning themselves for a feast.

He did not know that the Lacedæmonians always smoothed their hair before battle. He did not know that Lycurgus had said that long hair enhances manly beauty, while it makes masculine ugliness even more repulsive. The Persian horseman was much surprised.

Then Leonidas looked up by chance and saw the Persian, the glittering rider high above the serrated mountain comb, perhaps within arrow-shot.

For a minute Leonidas stared sharply at the Persian, who, for all he was stout-hearted enough, was frightened, though he kept his horse well in hand. Then Leonidas once more negligently dropped his eyes and, staring at the ground, continued in his position of an Achilles meditating before his tent, one knee crossed over the other, his chin resting in his hand.

The others also had seen the Persian. They gave

a fleeting glance upward, pointed with a finger, laughed and kept on running their races, casting their quoits or spears, or else, seriously, smoothing their hair.

The Persian horseman looked on much astonished. With the exception of this handful of men, there was no army to be seen in the pass of Thermopylæ, which measured several miles in length.

CHAPTER XXII

# THE SLAUGHTER OF THE IMMORTALS

WHEN the Persian scout had returned to the camp where Xerxes awaited him, and had made a report of his ride of reconnaissance to the King of Kings and his generals, they all burst into uncontrollable laughter. Xerxes doubted whether the scout could have seen clearly from such a height. Was he sure that he had recognized Leonidas? And hadn't he simply invented that story about the hair, because he had seen nothing at all? When Xerxes had recovered a little from his royal laughter, he sent for Demaretus, son of Ariston, whom he already had consulted on the terrace of the fortress of Doriscus. Demaretus came in haste and Xerxes spoke, while with a gracious gesture he invited the princely exile to be seated. This time Demaretus could not even seat himself at Xerxes' feet, since the king was seated on a small field-throne with a narrow step.

"Demaretus! Why do the Lacedæmonians in the pass of Thermopylæ act so strangely, that is, if there be any truth in what this scout has reported?"

"King!" said Demaretus. "I already spoke to you regarding this people when you went forth to war. When I mentioned my fears you laughed them to scorn. And hard as it may be for me to reveal the truth in the presence of your omnipotence, I shall nevertheless do so. Listen to me, I beg of you. These men, this handful of men, these few thousand men who surround him who is the King of Sparta in my stead, will contest your thoroughfare through the narrow pass. For the Lacedæmonians always smooth and comb their long hair when death threatens them. Conquer these men, O King, and neither the Spartans who have remained in their city, nor any people in the world will ever again rise against you! For the Spartans against whom you are marching are the bravest of all the Greeks. Their kingdom is the most prosperous state, and their city the fairest in all Hellas!"

Xerxes did not catch the melancholy that tinged the enthusiasm of the exile who stood before him. Unmoved he continued:

"How can a few thousand men fight my armies?"

He laughed loudly, and about him, just as loudly, laughed his brothers, his brothers-in-law and his nephews.

Demaretus merely said:

"Lord, call me a deceiver if that which I predict does not come to pass."

Demaretus retired. For four days the Persians remained inactive in the hills. Xerxes was waiting for the handful of men smoothing their hair, gathered about their mad king and general who sat before his tent on a boulder, dreaming, to take to flight. He would let them flee unmolested, thought he magnanimously, and admired himself because he smiled so good-naturedly at these poor fools in their folly. Yet on the fifth day he grew angry because they remained to challenge him with their impertinence. He commanded a detachment of Medes and Cissians to capture and parade them before him. All day long he waited impatiently for their return. Fresh troops marched out to see what had become of their comrades. When the Medes and Cissians came back they returned without prisoners, and their captains reported great losses suffered by them.

"How can that be possible?" cried Xerxes, in a rage.

One captain after another gave him the same answer:

"We have many men, Lord, but not many warriors."

The battle against the thick cluster of defenders in the narraw entrance resembling a fortress had lasted all day. Persian corpses lay heaped on the shore of the sea. Twenty thousand had been counted. On the following day Xerxes, to end the matter once and for all, ordered Hydarnes and his Immortals to capture the little troop and march it past his throne, his field-throne. So Hydarnes, radiant in golden armour, rode off to Anthela, amid his picked soldiers, the Immortals, to force Thermopylæ.

The fact that there were ten thousand of them did not help matters. And, actually, all ten thousand of them did not go. Perhaps six, or five, or three thousand of them went. Yet no matter how many of them went it could not alter the case. The pass between the rocks was so narrow that it was possible for only *one* man to fight against another. In addition, the lances of the Immortals were too short, and the picked soldiers appeared unable to make any headway, at least not against the Lacedæmonians. Many an Immortal bit the grass, and lay magnificently gold-scaled, the blood streaming from his cut throat, a hindrance to the man who came after him.

Then the Lacedæmonians seemed to flee, shoulder to shoulder, through the narrow pass. The Immortals followed them, roaring with bass voices drunken with victory. Yet the Lacedæmonians turned suddenly, and five of them, not more, fell upon the roaring Immortals with spear and sword. They slaughtered them under the eyes of the living wall of hundreds pressing after, who thought that the foremost already had gained ground.

Then the Lacedæmonians, again appearing to flee, regularly and almost mechanically repeated their cruel tactics. An unbelievable number of Immortals fell. It was no longer possible to step over their corpses between the narrow walls of rock. Hydarnes, raging, commanded a halt in order to carry the fallen back out of the way.

Xerxes, whose field-throne had been placed on a projecting crag, viewed the battle from that vantage point. He, too, raged. Thrice he rose in his anger. That was proof positive that the sight impressed him. As a rule he sat in great dignity when he watched a battle. But this was maddening. So he rose thrice. Toward evening the Persians beat a retreat. Along the shore of the sea was visible an endless procession of Immortals borne away on stretchers made of boughs. The Lacedæmonians carried their own fallen through the gates of the pass. They were so few in number that the Persians refused to believe the Greeks had so speedily gotten their dead out of the way.

It was then that the unavoidable, the fateful betrayer, Ephialtes, appeared before Xerxes.

## CHAPTER XXIII

## EPHIALTES

DURING the night Ephialtes led the Persians across the hills over a secret trail from Æsopus. Without the traitor the Persians never would have discovered this trail. At the hour when torches are lit Hydarnes with his Immortals followed Ephialtes, Past the rustling brush, under the thickly-leaved holm-oaks, in the sultry evil darkness they slunk along over hills that rose increasingly higher. All night long they marched in silence, most suspicious of the traitor who, perhaps, meant to sacrifice himself for his fatherland by a seeming betrayal. When they reached the top of the mountain, dawn broke in the east, glimmering between the tree-trunks.

The thousand heavy-armed hoplites from Phocis, who guarded the secret trail, were surprised, and astonished to hear the footsteps of the approaching Persians rustling through the countless leaves that had already fallen. The surprise was mutual. A cloud of Persian arrows drove the Phocians to the upper heights. The latter prepared to die. For there were several thousand Immortals. Yet these descended the hillside and paid no more attention to those who had flown higher up.

Then the Phocians understood.

## CHAPTER XXIV

## THE LAST NIGHT

THAT same night the soothsayer Megistias, after he had consulted the entrails of the victims, revealed for the first time to the astonished Greeks that if they remained, they would be surrounded in Thermopylæ by the Persians and would perish.

A council was held around Leonidas, and Leonidas told the disheartened, the reluctant and those who were contrary-minded that they might leave, lest they perish. He, however, would stay in Thermopylæ with three hundred Spartans, with the Thespians and the Theban hostages. Why need the others remain? They felt no desire to stay and await the certain death which the entrails of the sacrifices had promised them. They wished to serve their fatherland more effectively and circumspectly. So they said to Leonidas, who stood amidst his three hundred Lacedæmonians like the god Ares amid a handful of heroes; and they took down their tents, which they had with difficulty wedged among the moist, mossy clefts of the rock. They took their leave with many words, long speeches, even with ridicule, and also with emotion. Then they went.

Leonidas, quietly superior, even sped their departure, and that without any mockery or bitterness. They disappeared among the clefts and the caves, between the knotted oak-boles, along the broad pools of the warm baths, their copper greaves flashed in passing among the trampled fern and sedge and glimmered out in the distance. On their left they cast a stolen glance at the Ægean Sea, that lay vernally blue between the rocks and in the salt surfaces of the lagoons. Perhaps they were looking to see if they could discover the Persian fleet, though they knew it was not there and never could be there. Whoso is not calm expects the impossible in time of danger. Along the Melampygian Rock they vanished, detachment after detachment, one hundred after another, one thousand after another, and slunk off to Locris.

Thermopylæ was almost empty. In its narrows —measuring no more than fifty metres across from rocks which resembled petrified struggling Titans— the eye glancing down from the towering, perpendicular wall of stone, saw a little swarm of tiny white specks, hardly a hundred tents surrounding that of Leonidas.

## CHAPTER XXV

## THE WIND IN THE ROBES OF NIKE

LEONIDAS reflected. He was no genius, like Themistocles. He was no cunning statesman, no subtle thinker. In his great, simple soul there was no complication of contradictions. Within him all was clear, for him there existed only the vertical lines, not to be avoided, which he saw glimmer before him.

In addition, Leonidas reverenced the gods in whom he believed. And as he reflected, sitting before his tent among the rocks, as Achilles once sat on the Trojan strand, his thoughts were first of all concerned with how he and his men might escape being surrounded by the approaching Persians. His thoughts dwelt only on the oracle, which he recalled.

When at the beginning of the war the Lacedæmonians had questioned the Pythoness in Delphi, she had replied in verses of the ancient epic:

"To ye, however, who in spacious Sparta abide, I predict:
Either your great and famous capital city will perish
At the hands of Perseus' grandchildren, or, if this happen not,
She will mourn the death of her monarch, of Hercules' line."

Leonidas had become King of Sparta but a short time ago. His two older brothers had died. He had never imagined that the crown would fall to him. And this crown had been his no more than a few weeks. He thought of his brief day of royalty and admitted to himself that he would die fighting. He thought of his young wife Gorgo, daughter of his dead brother Cleomenes. He thought of his young son. He thought of the three hundred who had stayed with him, and who, all in the very bloom of manhood, had left women and children at home in Sparta.

Yet there was but little sorrow for all this in Leonidas' soul. Rather did there dwell in it, like a serene enthusiasm, the calm expectation that he would fight and die for his homeland, that he, surrounded by all his brave hearts, would be famous forevermore. Round about his smooth, meditative brow, in which was graven a single manly wrinkle, he heard the fluttering wings of broad-pinioned Nike. He felt the swelling winds of her white garments. He saw the white virginal arms of the goddess of victory reach out, and her fingers hand him the

[131]

branches and wreaths of myrtle and laurel. Amid the sheer rocks, where the sun of the fateful day— the first of many fateful days—was now shining, the radiant visions gleamed faintly as though framed in the golden sun-motes, about Leonidas, the meditating hero.

## CHAPTER XXVI

# THE PASSING OF THE THREE HUNDRED

ON THAT day which was to be his last, Leonidas gathered about him his three hundred Spartans, but also the Thebans, the hostages—the Thebans were Persian sympathizers—and the Thespians.

"Venerable father!" said Leonidas to the soothsayer, who had announced to him the unavoidability of what the entrails of the victims had declared, "Go! There is still time."

"Leonidas," Megistias replied. "When I have already ordered my only son to go, I yielded to a father's cowardice. He is still young, hardly more than a boy. I ordered him to go, and he went. I, however, shall stay."

"Then let us sit down to our funeral feast!" said Leonidas. "Eat, my friends, this morn, with the thought in mind that this evening ye shall sup in the palace of Hades!"

And all seated themselves in one place or another, on the rocks or in the grass, and ate.

Up on the hill where Xerxes had camped with the Immortals, the King of Kings that morning briskly went through the usual ceremonies in honour of the Sun. In the midst of the Magians his movements with goblet and amphora were solemn, pious and uplifting. Xerxes knew how to carry out such ceremonies with majestic gestures. Then the Persians marched down the hill, ten thousand in number, in a broad circle, to surround Thermopylæ. The traitor Ephialtes led them. The sergeants, lash in hand, drove the warriors down the hill before them.

Hitherto the reinforced wall at the entrance had protected the Lacedæmonians. But now, as the Persians staggered down the rocks from every side, Leonidas and his men pushed forward into the broadest portion of the pass. There they awaited the Persians, looking death in the eye, yet unafraid because of the ideal and the glory that shone before them. They meant to sell their lives and this pass to Locris for the highest possible price, and the exalted madmen fell upon the Persians with long spear and broadsword.

Whipped on by their sergeants, the first Persians were slain in the Greek attack. Lamenting, they flung themselves into the sea. They fell beneath the feet of those who were rumbling down the rocks behind them. They fell till the long Greek spears

[134]

splintered and the short Greek swords shivered against the Persian shields. Yet the Persians kept coming on and on, down the rocks, a glittering torrent of thousands of suns. Leonidas himself fought like a raging lion. The Persian spears, a cloud of long, sharp needles, fell upon him.

Suddenly, off yonder, Leonidas saw Ephialtes, the traitor, and then, then he saw Xerxes himself, encircled by his glittering captains and the Immortals. And fury possessed Leonidas so that he did not feel the splitting of his helmet and his bleeding head. He did not feel the blood running down all over his body from the slashes of darts· and spears. In the midst of his faithful men he pushed on toward the Persian king with sword upswung. His blue eyes flashed savagely. Ephialtes fled to one side, Xerxes himself was so surprised at the furious onset of the Spartan king, whose capture and appearance before him he had already ten times commanded, that he stood with his mouth wide open. He stood between his two younger brothers, Abrocomes and Hyperanthes, sons of Darius.

Quite unexpectedly, only a step behind him, Xerxes saw the two princes, his brothers, fighting with the roaring Lacedæmonians, man to man. The Spartans cut down the Immortals, they cut down the two princes. Leonidas himself drew near and set his foot on Abrocomes' corpse. And Xerxes, as though turned to stone, because the impossible was happening, seemed unable to defend himself. He stood with wide-open mouth, and could not realize that his two brothers lay dead, at his very feet, trampled by this madman, this visionary.

By now Leonidas had drawn quite near to Xerxes. Leonidas no longer had a spear, his spear was broken; he no longer had a sword, his sword was shattered. He raised both blood-dripping hands high in the air, spread them to grip, and flinging himself on Xerxes, tore off the diadem of the King of Kings and flung it in his face. Xerxes roared with pain and indignation, and the Immortals surrounded him with a wall of swords.

The Lacedæmonians surrounded Leonidas, who tottered and bled at every pore. Though close pressed they drew back and hid their dying king in their midst. Four times the cluster of men swayed back and forth, back and forth, in the narrow pass. Four times it seemed as though the Greeks would drive off the Persians, in the face of the grievous despair of Xerxes, who stood with fist outstretched by the corpses of his brothers. Yet now Ephialtes came up with swarms of newly-gathered soldiers. They descended the hills in clouds.

The Thebans now turned treacherous. They surrendered, cried that they were for Persia, always had been for Persia, always would be for Persia. Only the Lacedæmonians and the Thespians, in a serried group, the dying Leonidas in their midst, reached the hillock by the gate through which the enemy had entered. They ranged themselves behind the wall which no longer protected them, since the enemy converged upon them from all sides. There they continued to fight, with only here and there a sword to lift, but wrestling, gouging and tearing their foes with hands and teeth, until it seemed as though a mass of high-flung Persian shields, rattling and clattering, poured down upon them and buried them, that Persian spears pierced every body writhing beneath the clattering shields, and Persian swords

[136]

cut off every head that wrung itself out from under them.

The road to Delphi, to Athens, lay open.

* * *

Xerxes was ashamed of his losses. He sent a herald to his fleet, which lay between the Artemisian Cape and Histæia, off Eubœa, and invited the marines to visit the battlefield of Thermopylæ which Persia had so gloriously won.

The marines and the oarsmen came. They saw the bodies of a thousand fallen Persians, and paid them the last honours. All the other thousands had at Xerxes' command been hurriedly buried in the ravines where earth was shovelled over them, and fallen leaves. The fighting crews of the ships saw as well hundreds of fallen Greeks whom Xerxes had had piled up in the same place as a stage effect.

The ruse was all too transparent. The marines and oarsmen returned to the fleet the following day. They had heard and they understood. Their smiles and whispers betrayed that they had understood.

Thermopylæ remained open, free and abandoned.

* * *

In swarms the vultures had followed the flight of the two eagles which now and again were seen winging above the blue pools and the foaming ocean straits, above the gorges and between the holm-oaks. The wings of the vultures during the next days rustled over Thermopylæ like a dark cloud, fraught with evil omen.

The rustling of the vultures' wings did not endure. Yet that other rustling of wings which

Leonidas had heard about his head like a harmony and a music, when he sat lost in thought before his tent, did endure. And this other beat of wings—not of vultures' pinions, but the rustling of the pure wings of the white goddesses of victory, and the soft rustling of their robes—has endured for centuries. And with it endures the rustling of the waving branches and wreaths of myrtle and laurel bestowed on those children of immortality who in that place had fought the incomparable battle of heroes around Leonidas, their blond Spartan king, the heroes who succeeded him.

## CHAPTER XXVII

## DEMARETUS' COUNSEL

WHEN Xerxes had returned to camp he sent for Demaretus to come to his tent. Xerxes was seated on a tent-throne. His brother Achæmenes, whom he had appointed high admiral of his fleet, sat at his right hand. With a gesture Xerxes invited Demaretus to sit on his left, on a vacant stool. Sunlight streamed through the red silken hangings of the great tent. In it stood Xerxes' gilded couch with lion-skins, his gilded dresser, with its golden toilet accessories, and his gilded wash-table with its golden ewers and vases. In it hung Xerxes' golden armour, and the king and the prince were seated at a gilded table on which lay a map of Hellas. All this gilt and gold glittered in the glowing sunshine with the rich radiance of which Xerxes was so fond.

"Demaretus!" said Xerxes amiably. "You are an honest man. I have proved the truth of your words. What you prophesied has come to pass. Now tell me how many Lacedæmonians still remain in Sparta. And are they all as brave as those who fought against us?"

Xerxes did not like to speak Leonidas' name. On his brow there was a scar from the diadem which had been flung in his face, and the diadem itself had been trodden completely out of shape.

The King of Kings smiled kindly at Demaretus.

"O King!" Demaretus replied. "The Lacedæmonians are numerous and their towns are many, yet I shall tell you what you wish to know. Sparta, the capital of Lacedæmon, contains eighteen thousand men like those three hundred whom you overcame."

Demaretus, once King of Sparta, also forbore to mention Leonidas' name, though the words "around Leonidas" were at his tongue's end.

"The other Lacedæmonians"—Demaretus vaguely felt he should add—"are brave, yet not with the unexampled bravery of the three hundred."

Again Demaretus forbore to mention Leonidas' name.

"Whom you slew," repeated Demaretus, who had once been King of Sparta.

"Tell me," insisted the king, "how I can most easily master them. For, in truth, it is taking too long."

"Great King," said Demaretus, "I will advise you to the best of my knowledge. Send three hundred of your ships to the island of Cytherea, off the Lacedæmonian coast. From there threaten Sparta, which always fears a fleet. Lay siege to Lacedæmon from that point and the rest of Hellas will fall into your hands. For your army on land can easily vanquish Hellas if Sparta already has her hands full and cannot come to her aid. If you do not take my advice you will have to fight a hard battle on the Corinthian isthmus."

Then Achæmenes rose in a passion. He hated Demaretus, the exile, to whom his brother Xerxes continually appealed for advice.

He cried violently:

"Brother and King! Will you lend an ear to one who envies you your good fortune and whose service does not profit you? Is he not like all the Greeks, who envy the good fortune of others and are full of hatred for their superiors? You have already lost four hundred ships in the storm. If you send three hundred other ships to cruise off the Peloponnesian coast, will not our enemies be the stronger? If we keep our fleet together we cannot be vanquished. If the land army and the fleet keep in touch each can aid the other. If you separate them they are useless to each other."

Xerxes was in a gentle, condescending mood.

"Achæmenes!" said he, while a magnanimous smile played about his blue-black beard, "your advice seems good to me, and I shall probably take it. Yet Demaretus is an honest man and my guest. His counsel is always worth hearing and I do not wish to have any evil spoken of him."

[141]

After Achæmenes and Demaretus had left the tent Xerxes began to consider and weigh their advice.

"Three hundred ships to the Peloponnesian coast or not?"

He meditated till late at night and could not sleep.

## CHAPTER XXVIII

## SCYLLIAS THE DIVER

THE Greek fleet steered for the Artemisian promontory, the most northern point of the island of Eubœa. The Corinthians had forty ships; the Megarians, twenty; the Chalcidians also had twenty, lent them by the Athenians. The Æginetæ had eighteen ships; the Sicyonians, twelve; the Lacedæmonians, twenty; the Epidaurians, eight; the Eretrians, seven; the Trœzenians, five. The inhabitants of Styrus had two ships and so had those of the island of Cios, while the Locrians had seven. Many of these ships had fifty oarsmen, and they steered through the broad, agitated waters of the Ægean Sea.

The Athenians also pointed a course for the Artemisian promontory, with a hundred and twenty-seven ships. Eurybiades, son of Euryclides—for the allies would have no Athenian admiral—was in command of the entire fleet.

Owing to political expediency and a patriotic love for Hellas as a whole, Athens had not insisted upon the admiralty. In spite of their many ships they yielded, for the time being, and Themistocles yielded, while, cunning as he was, he hatched out various genial intrigues. The captains of the Greek fleet lying off Artemisia, as they stared at the tremendous Persian armada—it was still tremendous in spite of its repeated mishaps—were filled with terror and thought of flight. The Eubœans begged Eurybiades to wait until they had put their women, children and slaves in a place of refuge. They could not induce him to promise.

They went to Themistocles.

They offered him thirty talents if he could hold the fleet off their island, so that the naval battle would not be fought elsewhere and Eubœa left defenceless. Themistocles smiled as he beheld the thirty talents outspread before him. He saw no treason in allowing Hellenes to bribe him for Hellas' good. Nor did he think it a scoundrelly trick to bride Hellenic sea-captains, with Hellenic money, not to leave these waters for the benefit of Hellas. He took three talents and went to Adimantus, the captain of the Corinthians, who was preparing to weigh anchor, and said to him:

"Adimantus! By Zeus Omnipotent! Surely you do not mean to leave us! If you remain I will give you an even greater gift than the King of Persia would give you if you went!"

He gave him the three talents. And Adimantus stayed, thinking it was Athenian money he had received.

Themistocles went to Eurybiades with five talents. And Eurybiades, too, was convinced that he had been given Athenian money.

The rest of the talents that had come from Eubœa Themistocles kept for himself. There were two and twenty of them. He had not been dishonest, but only cunning, and, content with himself and with Hellas, he smiled on all men and all things. It was then that a man and a young girl were led before Themistocles. Both were dripping with water.

"Who are you?" Themistocles asked.

"Themistocles, son of Neocles!" said the man. "I am Scyllias of Scione, the most famous diver of Hellas. And behold! beside me is my daughter Cyane. She dives as well as I do. When the Persian fleet was visited by the tempest off Mount Pelion, we both dove down into the depths of the sea in spite of the raging storm."

"And tore the Persian anchors loose," said Cyane, laughing.

"But I brought the Persians many gold and silver vessels from the bottom of the sea," said the diver slyly.

"Yet we kept some for ourselves," added Cyane, and laughed again.

Themistocles laughed as well.

"And now?" he asked.

"We no longer wish to live among the Persians," said Scyllias.

"We wish to return to the Hellenes," added Cyane.

"I dove into the water at Aphetæ, where the Persian fleet lies at anchor."

"I, too," said Cyane.

"I did not come to the surface till I reached Cape Artemisia."

"I, too," said Cyane.

Themistocles laughed.

"That's not true," he said, still laughing.

"Not true?" cried Scyllias indignantly.

"Not true?" echoed his daughter.

"How long a stretch do you claim you swam under water?" Themistocles queried, still laughing. He himself figured it out. "Eighty stadia?"

"Small stadia," said the diver, somewhat more humble.

Themistocles continued to laugh.

"You came in a boat," he said.

"Yet first we swam under water," said Cyane. "The boat was waiting for us."

"Oh, well! Of course, we did not swim eighty stadia under water," the cunning diver admitted.

All three laughed. Then Scyllias said:

"I am a true Greek. You can trust me. The Persian fleet—at least part of it—is putting out for Eubœa. I only wanted you to know this. And what I said about the Persian anchors is true."

"I believe you," laughed Themistocles. "I will advise the captains of the fleet to consult with you."

That morning a counsel was held. And that same afternoon the small, incomplete little Greek fleet sailed out to meet the navy of Persia in order to show what it could do.

The captains and soldiers on the Persian ships

thought that a few individual Greek madmen were under way with a few ships. They hauled up their anchors and thought they would capture these insane Greeks with ease.

The Greeks advanced to the attack. And in the narrow straits they captured thirty Persian triremes.

That night a tremendous storm broke, and it almost seemed as though Boreas and the other gods of the wind were still protecting the Greeks. It was midsummer. The thunder rolled without ceasing down from Mount Pelion, together with heavy clouds and a clattering rain. Many Persian ships were wrecked, and the corpses and wreckage became entangled in the other vessels' banks of oars.

And all this came to pass because Zeus, the god of the Greeks, struggling with the god of the Persians, whom they also called Zeus, wished to reduce the Persian fleet to an equality with the Greek. The Persian ships were mercilessly flung against the Eubœan reefs, and at daybreak the Greeks sent reinforcements—fifty-three Athenian ships—and that same afternoon destroyed the Cilician squadron of the Persian fleet.

On the third day they fought on an equal basis. The Persian fleet, so hampered by its own numerous ships that they strayed into each other's tiers of oars and rammed each other, lost a countless number of men and vessels that day. The Greeks, too, suffered severe losses. It was the same day on which Leonidas defended Thermopylæ. On land and on sea the Greeks were defending the entrances to southern Hellas.

That evening, however, the Greeks, and the Athenians in particular, upon their return from

Artemisia, considered the greatness of their losses, and consulted together as to how they might most swiftly escape into the island seas of Greece.

But that was not what Themistocles desired, and he thought:

"If only I could induce the Ionians and Carians to rejoin us."

On the rocks above the springs that yielded potable water, and where the Persian crews must necessarily come to drink, he caused to be written the following words:

"Ionians! You do wrong when you fight against your blood-brothers and seek to force us Hellenes under the Persian yoke. Do not forget that you are the cause of this war! At least, if the Persians compel you against your will, hold back as much as you can. Do not put your heart into fighting against your fathers and brothers!"

Themistocles thought:

"If Xerxes does not learn of these inscriptions, the Ionians will pass over to us. But if Xerxes gets wind of them the Ionians will become suspect in his eyes, and he will not allow them to fight with his fleet."

A spy came from Thracis and reported the death of Leonidas, of the three hundred, and of the Thespians, and that the road to Athens lay open.

They were days weighed with care, well-nigh days of despair. It was not advisable to lie longer in these foreign waters, even though the whole fleet were to be destroyed here. How frail was this wooden wall, this proud, yet already sorely tried fleet of the youthful sea-power, which could count only upon the waves, but no longer on the land, so necessary to man!

## CHAPTER XXIX

## THE ARCADIANS

SOME discontented Arcadians who did not care
for fighting but wanted only to plough, sow
and reap, came to Phocis and appeared before
Xerxes and his staff.

"What are the Greeks in Elis, Achaia, Argolis
and Arcadia doing now?" Xerxes asked them with
a frown. "Are they making ready to withstand
us?"

"No, Lord!" said the spokesman of the Arcadians.

"Then what are they doing?" asked Xerxes.

"The Olympian Games are in progress at

Olympia," said the Arcadian. "They are having horse races and chariot races there, and athletic contests, O King!"

"What is the prize awarded the victor?"

"Sometimes it is a tripod, but often it is no more than a wreath of olive," replied the Arcadian. "The olive wreath is probably the prize most sought after. The most violent contests are those waged for the olive wreath."

"What sort of people is this to which you are leading us, Mardonius?" cried Tritantæchmes, son of Artabanus. "About to be conquered by us, they are running races and engaging in athletic contests at Olympia for the sake of an olive wreath! Do they all fight for fame's sake, like that Leonidas at Thermopylæ?"

Xerxes frowned discontentedly.

"Nephew Tritantæchmes," he said, "it is all a question of culture. I can't understand why you don't see it. Our culture is on a higher level than that of the Greek. All that we know about political economy and administration would revolt against such a piece of folly as the playing of athletic games on the eve of fate's fulfilment. We Persians are more sensible by nature. We—for argument's sake I am admitting that we might be defeated, though this is impossible because the god of the Persians aids us and will continue to aid us—would certainly not try on the eve of such a decision . . ."

"And still I think it magnificent," said Tritantæchmes.

His nephew's interruption made Xerxes angry. Not alone his nephew, but even the simple Arcadian interrupted the King of Kings after Tritantæchmes and good-naturedly said:

"Lord! Down there they do not believe they will be defeated, nor do we Arcadians. We have not come here because we think you will be victorious, Lord, but because we want to work. We are in need of the barest necessities, and we are farmers rather than warriors. We would very much like to have work, Lord, and plough and reap and harvest, if by so doing we can earn our keep."

When, as now, Xerxes' sense of royal dignity was wounded, which happened off and on, what with so many brothers, brothers-in-law and nephews, and in this case first by his nephew and then by this Arcadian peasant, he had the good taste to control his anger. So on this occasion he merely said to his staff of glittering captains, ranked behind him:

"I had always thought that the Arcadians were poetic, at least more poetic than this hind. This Arcadian does not especially impress me, but we can lease him some meadows here in conquered Phocis."

About the lips of the glittering brothers, brothers-in-law and nephews played a grateful, aristocratic smile. Xerxes allowed the Arcadians to depart in peace. And they cultivated the conquered land of Phocis and thought of the future.

## CHAPTER XXX

## EARTHQUAKE IN ATHENS

XERXES set out for Athens.
But he sent a division of his army off to the right, to Delphi. He would have preferred first to go to Delphi himslf. But he was afraid of Delphi. He shuddered at the mere thought of the oracle. So with a sidelong look to the right, at Parnassus, the holy hill on which Phœbus Apollo throned and on whose slopes the Muses danced their rounds to choral song over luxuriant flowery meadows, Xerxes set out for Athens.

Along the Cephissus the towns of Drymus, Elatea, Hyampolis and Parapotamii were burning.

The temples went up in flames. At Abæ the temple of Apollo was looted. These things were not always done at Xerxes' command, yet the torch of war and the greed of the Barbarians were accountable. Along the road the raped women lay dying. The despair of this mercilessly conquered and trampled land across which the wild hordes stormed was all that was left in this mythically holy countryside which had echoed the conquerer's tread, and the gods were silent.

The Delphians—after the oracle, in their question whether they should bury the sacred temple treasure or carry if off, had replied with arrogant incomprehensibility—had sent their wives and children to Corinth, and themselves fled up the ridges of Parnassus to Amphissa.

Only sixty men remained as temple servants about the prophet Aceratus, whose business it was to frame verbally the oracular fragments stammered by the Pythoness. On the night the Persian army division approached the holy city, the lowering black sky was full of clouds. Under cover of this strange, untimely darkness the Persian robbers drew near. They met with no resistance, yet many of them wished they had not been chosen for the work in hand. It occurred to them that Phœbus Apollo might be identical with Ormuzd, though the one was the god of the Greeks and the other the god of the Persians. And this sky, dark before the time, and filled with heavy, tragically depressing clouds, was eloquent of evil and divine rage on this summer day. The driving clouds floated about Parnassus, hardly visible, and ill-omened lightnings flashed continually from their dark masses. After all, this was a strange land in which they, the victors, found

[153]

themselves, while alien gods dwelt up yonder and were wroth at them. They themselves were separated from the millions of the mighty host, and hardly felt like victors, but more like robbers seeking their spoil in the middle of the night.

The awesome outlines of the massive temple stood out against the black cloud-battlements, now and again illumined by vivid flashes of lightning. The marble columns gleamed ghostly white, and the gabled triangles of the roof looked unreal to the advancing Persians in those uncanny surroundings. And the square walls round about also stood out with a ghost-white gleam like divine, unconquerable hindrances. Above the open arena of the theatre seemed to float great shadows, as though divine spirits were there enacting their holy drama.

The Persians saw these strange things from the rocky path they were descending. The rain poured, the tempest raged more furiously. On their right rose the temple of Athene Pronæa.

Suddenly the earth trembled. The ground beneath the feet of the Persian horsemen shook. From Athene's temple sonorous voices and war-cries rang out, there sounded a terrific clatter of arms, as though the goddess herself were approaching. From Parnassus gigantic blocks of stone rolled down, as though the god were seeking to crush those who came to desecrate his temple. At the same time the Persians who already had reached Apollo's temple saw the prophet. He pointed to a heap of weapons that flashed in the lightning—bucklers, lances, swords and helmets—the sacred arms of Apollo himself, never touched or moved from their appointed place. There they lay, an awesome mass of sparkling metal, before the temple gate, and the prophet cried:

"A miracle! A miracle! The sacred arms no man may touch have removed themselves to this spot!"

The boulders tumbled down the mountain slopes in avalanches so tremendous that they seemed cast by the Titans. The earth trembled. Here, there and everywhere the Persians fled in terror, and two supernatural warriors of gigantic size, Phylacus and Autonous, the heroes of those regions, pursued them. The following morning the road at the foot of Mount Parnassus was sown with Persian corpses.

## CHAPTER XXXI

### LETTERS HOME

**X**ERXES sent a courier of the royal mail from Athens with a letter to Atossa and one to Amestris, to announce his victory.

The royal mail had been invented and instituted by Cyrus. It was one of the marvels of Persian administration. The posting houses were organized in military style, and lay at short distances from each other. Fresh horses stood ready saddled, and fresh couriers were in waiting at all these stations, always on the watch.

A courier trotted up with the mail-bag strapped to his person. He dismounted, and undid the mail-bag. The relief courier strapped it on, and swiftly leaped into the saddle of his waiting horse. He disappeared in a cloud of dust, riding furiously to the next station.

So it was that the royal mail came from Athens to Susa in fourteen days.

Atossa and Amestris read aloud their letters, which were almost identical:

"With the aid of Persia's god we have won a glorious victory. Athens is in our power. The enemy is fleeing from us on every side. His losses are beyond counting. Great treasure has fallen into our hands. Our losses are trifling. The god of Persia will continue to aid us. (Signed) Xerxes, King of Kings."

The queen and the princesses knew letters of this kind by heart. This time, however, the conquest announced—Athens—must be more important than the notice that, with the aid of Persia's god, Mount Athos had been pierced, or that one or another little known city in Thrace or Thessaly had been captured. Athens! Wasn't that tantamount to Hellas itself?

"The war is nearly over," decided Parmys, and Phaidyme came to the same conclusion.

Artozostra said happily:

"I have a letter from Mardonius. Allhighest Mother Atossa! Do you wish me to read Mardonius' letter aloud?"

The queen and the princess, crouching on their couches in a broad circle—Atossa with her inseparable whip and her evilly narrowed eyes, Amestris at the loom on which she was weaving a golden mantle for Xerxes—read each other their letters. It was good sport.

[157]

Xerxes did not write that Leonidas had torn the diadem from his brow.

Autumn was approaching. From the outer porticoes came the fragrant aroma of preserved peaches and pears.

## CHAPTER XXXII

## THE WOODEN WALLS

OWING to the insistence of the Athenians, the Hellenic fleet had left the Artemisian Cape and steered to Salamis, where it cast anchor. All women and children left Athens and fled to Salamis, to Trœzene, to Ægina. The oracle was fulfilled. The sacred serpent in Athene's temple on the Acropolis no longer ate its honey-cakes, a proof that Athene herself had left the city dedicated to her.

The Peloponnesians, who were to have defended Bœotia, before Athens, thought only of saving themselves, and were building a wall straight across the Isthmus of Corinth.

[159]

Xerxes drew near. And Fate seemed to approach with him. Before Salamis—in the radiant summer weather, it seemed as though heaven and the gods mocked at the disaster which had overtaken Athens —lay the Hellenic fleet. There were sixteen Spartan triremes, forty Corinthian, fifteen Sicyonian, ten Epidaurian, fifty Trœzenian, three Hermonian—all Peloponnesian vessels. There were one hundred and eighty Athenian ships, the most splendid fleet of all. The Æginetæ had twenty-four swift-rowing vessels, admirable under sail. The Chalcidians had twenty, the Eretrians had seven—they had already fought off the Artemisian Cape. Then there were those of Cios, of Naxos, of Melus, Siphnus and Seriphus: they relieved the four and twenty swift-rowing vessels. Aside from these lesser craft, three hundred and forty-eight triremes rocked on the blue sea before Salamis, in the narrow waters between that island and Mount Ægaleos.

The captains gathered about Eurybiades, in Salamis.

An Athenian messenger entered.

"The Barbarians are in Athens," he reported.

At once all was confusion. Many wished to sail off immediately with their ships, others were in favour of an eleventh-hour defence of the Corinthian isthmus. Discouragement paralysed the bravest, though because of their jealousy they did not like Athens, which had so grown in power, yet now had been completely crushed by Fate.

"They have swung the torch throughout Attica," reported the messenger. "Thespiæ is burning and Platæa."

"It is no more than three months ago that they crossed the Hellespont," murmured the captains of the fleet. One Greek clan reproached the other for all sorts of things. They all blamed one another.

Athens had been abandoned, the messenger continued. Only a few poor, aged men had fortified themselves on the Acropolis behind the wooden palisades, as the Pythoness had ordered.

There was audible a despairing hum of deep bass voices.

"This handful of poor wretches attempted to defend the citadel. Xerxes with his army occupied the Areopagus, opposite the Acropolis. His soldiers were crushed by the great rocks which these pitiable yet glorious defenders rolled down on them when they approached the sacred gates." Something like admiration sounded in the murmur of voices.

"Then the Barbarians discovered the secret passage between the steepest rocks. Had not the oracle foretold that the Persians would take possession of all that Athens owned on land? When its defenders saw the Barbarians within the Acropolis they slew one another, flung themselves from the walls, or fled into the interior of the temple. But the Barbarians killed them, in spite of the olive branches they held out to them, and looted the temple. Temple and citadel are now in ruins."

"We will restore both in their glory!" cried Themistocles, stepping forward, unaware that he was prophesying the advent of the age of Pericles.

The fleet commanders about Eurybiades, the admiral, considered whether they should leave Salamis and defend their fatherland at the Isthmus of Corinth.

Themistocles thought it certain that the allies, once they had cleared the waters of Salamis, would scatter and each return to his own country. He did not say so aloud. But when he was back on his own deck he discussed the matter in detail with his friend Mnesiphilus.

"Suppose the allies up anchor?" said Mnesiphilus. They looked at each other with one thought.

"Then Hellas is lost," said Themistocles.

"No one, not even Eurybiades, will be able to restrain the allies," said Mnesiphilus. "Themistocles, call another council."

Once more Themistocles spoke with passion and insistence. Yet Adimantus, the commander of the Corinthian ships, rudely interrupted him.

"Themistocles! In the foot-race those who hasten to cross the line before the others, to gain the goal, get a crack from the staff of the Hellanodike."

"True!" said Themistocles, without taking offence. "But those who hang back win no laurel wreaths."

Again he refrained from saying what he thought —that the allies would scatter if they decided to leave Salamis—and advanced other considerations.

"Eurybiades!" he cried imploringly. "The fortunes of all Hellas lie in your hand. You will save her if you offer the enemy battle in these waters, and refuse to listen to those who would have you leave Salamis. Listen to me and consider what I say. At the Isthmus our ships, since they are heavier and less numerous than those of the Persians, will have to engage on the open sea. We will lose Salamis, Megara and Ægina. The land army of the Barbarians will follow their armada, and flood the Peloponnesus. And the land of our gods will be exposed to the gravest danger. Take my advice. Then in these narrow straits, which favour us, we will win a glorious victory with our handful of ships. I feel it, I know it—positively. Round about are voices that whisper it to me. Must we not continue to protect Salamis, filled with our women and children? And if you fight here, will you not be protecting the Peloponnesus even better than at Corinth? Our enemies—I know that none can deny it—will disperse in sudden terror once we have defeated them at sea. We shall destroy their millions if only we are sensible. But if we act foolishly even the gods of Greece will be unable to save us."

Then Adimantus waxed wroth—for his mind was set on Corinth—and he cried:

"Are we to consider sensible only what you demand, Themistocles? For Eurybiades to save your homeland, which no longer exists, is that the only sensible thing to do? Show me your homeland, Themistocles! Show me your home city! Where are Attica and Athens? Where are they? They are in the power of Xerxes and his Barbarians!"

"My homeland and my home city," Themistocles cried furiously, "Attica and Athens, are where, at this moment, they are more powerful than Corinth —on the decks of over two hundred ships, manned by Athenians. Not a state in Hellas could withstand us, although our fleet is now our sole reliance. Remain at Salamis, Eurybiades, and you will save all Greece. What have we Greeks left but our ships? Or leave Salamis. In that case, however, we will sail off with our wives, our children and our slaves, to Siris, in Italy, which we already have so long possessed. There, according to the words of the oracle, we will found the cities promised us. Yet you, all of you"—he threatened them all in his rage —"will be abandoned by your allies as we have been, and have reason to mourn your fate!"

[163]

At this moment there was an earthquake. The sea trembled, the waves raised the other vessels around the admiral's flagship high in the air.

Then gradually the waters grew calm again.

It seemed as though the gods—those of Hellas, not of Persia—had spoken.

Thank-offerings were made to the gods, as well as to the heroes Ajax and Telamon, so that their shades might take part in the battle to come.

COLLEGE LIBRARY
ST.
JOSEPH'S
COLLEGE
1852
Phila., Pa.

[164]

## CHAPTER XXXIII

## THE IACCHIC HYMN

IN ATHENS Xerxes had recalled various Athenian expatriates to their natal city. One among them, Dicæus, son of Theocydes, was an old friend of Demaretus, the banished King of Sparta. One of those days before the battle they spent together, wandering about sadly outside the walls of Athens. It seemed as though the exile who had been recalled felt unable to breathe in this Athens to which a Persian king, with what seemed to be magnanimous calculation, had summoned him. And it seemed that the banished king, approaching Sparta with an enemy army, in spite of the fulfilment which soon promised to crown his ambition, could breathe no more freely than his Athenian friend.

The two men had strayed about on the slopes of Mount Ægaleos, which rises like a wall between Athens and Eleusis, the holy city of the mysteries, animatedly discussing the events of the day, hopeful or depressing, according to the point of view, and had reached the Thriasian plain. It stretched before them, in part sere heath, in part a grassy waste with long waving tufts of furze. The Persians had crossed it before entering Athens. On this sandy track, in this stony wilderness the traces of their march were still visible: shards of pottery where they had camped, the hides and offal of the slaughtered cattle they had eaten. Here and there the ruin of a burned house of farmstead thrust its black, distorted outlines into the blue-grey and sultry air.

It was a season of earthquakes. Both Greeks and Persians, considered them favourable prognostics. The two men, Demaretus and Dicæus, had wandered on, talking eagerly, gesticulating broadly and freely, in this lonely waste, this solitude which the people avoided. They stumbled over the stones and through the sand, and pushed farther away from Athens than they were aware. The sun began to sink behind Eleusis. The holy city, with the far-flung outline of its temple to Demeter, darkled in sombre stretches off in the distance. Vultures hung in the air.

"We must return," said Dicæus, "we are already quite close to Eleusis."

"The light and air about us here are awesome," said Demaretus, looking around. Suddenly he pointed to something at their very feet, something which, as they had approached, had been hidden by a boulder.

"Look!"

He pointed and clung to the arm of his friend. But it was only a woman's corpse, which, horrible to look at, already had been half-devoured by carrion birds.

"No, look yonder!" cried Dicæus, as he in turn pointed into the distance.

The two men, clinging the one to the other, peered together. There was no wind, and still across the plain there drew near something resembling a tremendous cloud of dust like that stirred up by a marching army. Yet there was no sound of voices, of steps, till suddenly . . .

"Hark!" cried Dicæus. "Hark!"

He stood silenced, stark with terror. Demaretus, shuddering, did not at first understand. Yet as he listened he heard a clear, chanting voice.

"Is someone singing out yonder?" he asked, refusing to believe his ears.

"Someone is singing the hymn of Iacchus," whispered Dicæus, who was beyond measure horrified at the supernatural mystery taking place at this late hour of the afternoon, under this strangely sombre sky, with a blood-red sunset shimmering through thick clouds of dust.

And, in fact, in solemn mystic tones rang out in the distance:

"Iacchus! O Iacchus!"

"What does it mean?" asked Demaretus.

"You don't know?" queried Dicæus. "Were you never initiated into the Eleusinian mysteries?"

"No," confessed Demaretus. "Tell me . . ."

"It is the sacred hymn which is sung on the sixth day of the mysteries, on the twentieth of the month Boëdromion, when the image of Bacchus Iacchus is carried in procession. It is terrifying to hear it in this silent plain, in this deserted wilderness. For yonder, Demaretus, yonder in that singing cloud of dust moves or floats a divinity! Demaretus! It foretells some great misfortune, a misfortune for Xerxes. Look! It is moving away from Eleusis!" The vultures circled about the heads of the two men.

"Whither is it floating?" asked Demaretus, watching apprehensively as he clung to the arm of his friend. "To the allies," said the initiate of Eleusis. "Beyond all question to the allies. Only note how it floats. If it drifts to the Peloponnesus, southward, the Persian land army will be destroyed."

"But it is floating eastward! It is floating eastward!" cried Demaretus, pointing in that direction.

"Then," cried Dicæus, "the fleet of Xerxes at Salamis will be destroyed. Hark, how clearly the hymn rings out!"

And, in truth, mysteriously, inexplicably from out the drifting cloud pealed the song.

"Iacchus! O Iacchus!"

Demaretus, his hand still clutching Dicæus' arm, whispered in the darkness now falling:

"Dicæus! Never mention this. Else neither you nor I would survive."

"No."

"Never mention that the gods protect us—proscripts that we are. . . . And the Persians . . ."

The two men fled down into the plain. They stumbled over the rocks. And the vultures that their passing had disturbed, dropped back upon the woman's corpse.

[168]

CHAPTER XXXIV

## BENEATH THE GOLDEN SAIL

THE Persian fleet lay at anchor off the port
towns of Phaleron and Piræus, and Xerxes
entered his own Sidonian vessel and seated
himself on his naval throne. All the fleet commanders, superior and inferior, had been summoned
to a council. For the Persians, no less than the
Greeks, had to decide whether they would fight a
naval battle here at Salamis.

When Xerxes had seated himself on his throne
beneath the golden sail, all the others—among them
the kings of Sidon and Tyre, and Queen Artemisia
of Halicarnassus—all sat. Mardonius asked the

[169]

opinion of each in turn. All, Mardonius included, thought that the battle should be fought. When Mardonius asked Queen Artemisia, however, saying: "Artemisia, you who have already proved yourself a heroine in our midst at Eubœa, give us your candid opinion," she said:

"Mardonius, I believe we should spare our fleet, that we should not provoke a naval battle. The Greeks are superior to the Persians at sea, in the same degree that men are superior to women. Is it absolutely necessary to venture a sea-fight? Is not Xerxes lord of Athens? Has he not reached his goal? Will not the rest of Hellas inevitably fall into the hands of the Persians? Listen! If we leave our ships as much as possible in harbour here, and advance across the Isthmus into the Peloponnesus, we will be victorious. The Greeks will no longer oppose us.

"You, Mardonius, will drive them back into their cities. They are unprovisioned in Salamis, and if you advance into the Peloponnesus, the Peloponnesians will not quietly remain in Salamis. What interest will they have in fighting before Athens? Yet if you decide on a naval battle I fear that defeat at sea will be followed by defeat on land. For all our thousands of allies—tell Xerxes this, Mardonius!— are slaves, inferior slaves, unreliable slaves—Egyptians, Cyprians, Cilicians, Pamphylians."

Xerxes had a high regard for Artemisia, though he was anything but a feminist at his own court in Susa. But if he thought it better for a queen to rule the royal household with a whip, like his mother Atossa, or to weave golden mantles of state, like his wife Amestris, rather than to fight in battle, in this particular instance he greatly prized Artemisia. He

[170]

thought the Amazon cut a picturesque figure at sea, among his captains of greater and lesser rank. She wore her helmet, beneath which flowed her black hair, with taking effect, and her short mailed tunic revealed her calves, protected by shining greaves. Xerxes regarded Artemisia with a certain æsthetic tenderness. When Mardonius, in accordance with the rules governing a Persian council of war, acquainted him with Artemisia's advice, he in no wise agreed with what the queen said. Yet at the same time he smiled at her with great amiability. He thought her unique, unique of her kind, and yet . . .

The final result of the splendid gathering was that Xerxes decided in favour of a naval battle. He had, in fact, reached this decision before he had summoned the council. This was Xerxes' method of procedure in nearly all cases. And, incidentally, he had his own entirely personal ideas and inspirations just as well as Artemisia of Halicarnassus had. His thoughts and inspirations of the moment he communicated to Mardonius, while the radiant kings, the queen, the fleet captains of greater or lesser degree—all resplendent in chains of honour and numerous armlets—descended into their launches when the council was over.

"Mardonius," said Xerxes, "I admit that we were unlucky last month at Eubœa. The marines did not do their duty there. Our fleet should have defeated the smaller Greek one. It all happened, however, bcause I was not there in person. Up yonder, from my throne—command that it be set up in an advantageous spot!—I shall witness the sea-fight at Salamis. With the aid of the Persian god we will destroy the trifling Greek fleet."

That night Mardonius marched off with the land

forces to the Peloponnesus. He was informed that
the Greek confederates—Arcadians, Elians, Corin-
ians, Sicyonians, Epidaurians, Phliasians, Trœzenians and Hermonians—were building a high wall
across the Isthmus. They were building it under
the command of Cleombrotus, Leonidas' brother.

## CHAPTER XXXV

## THE PEDAGOGUE

A S SOON as the Greeks before Salamis had learned from their spies that Xerxes had decided to fight at sea, they were much dismayed. The same consultations which had been held the week preceding were repeated. Most of the allies reproached Eurybiades for his inconceivable carelessness in continuing to lie off Salamis with a fleet so inferior in numbers to the Persian armada. Themistocles, with the Athenians, the Æginetæ and the Megarians remained obstinately of the opinion that only at Salamis was Greek salvation to be found.

But Themistocles began to get bored, especially

[173]

when he saw that his opponents would be victorious, and it would be decided that the fleet should leave the waters of Salamis. He crept out of the council, sent for Sicinnus, his children's tutor and his own confidant, and said:

"Row to the Persian fleet in a boat!"

"To the Median fleet," corrected the pedagogue. It was a more or less patriotically coloured purism which led the Greeks to call the Persians, who had become one people together with the vanquished Medians, Medes.

Themistocles shruggd his shoulders.

"I order you to row to the Persian fleet and tell Xerxes . . ."

Themistocles whispered three long sentences in the tutor's ear.

"Can you remember that?" Themistocles asked.

"Yes," said the tutor. "My message will signify Hellas' salvation and the destruction of the Medes."

Again Themistocles shrugged his shoulders at the word "Medes." The tutor rowed off in a boat with two men, as though for a pleasure trip. The sea was calm. Dolphins played among the waves. The sky shone radiant with the splendid blue of midsummer. The tutor doubled the Cynosuran promontory. The coast lines and reefs, the rocks beyond the island of Psyttalea showed blue as though misted with purer light. There lay the Persian fleet, in all its tremendous extent. It seemed hardly to rest on the lightly moving waves. Ship was aligned with ship. The sails had been reefed. The long oars had been drawn in. The rigging was outlined in dark tracery against the deep, trembling blue of the southern sky.

The tutor waved a white cloth.

The Medes saw him. He waved, he approached.

It seemed strange to him that he, together with two men in a boat, should draw near the tremendous Median armada.

Could he speak to the King of Kings, he called out—putting his hands to his mouth—to deliver to him a message from the admiral of the Athenian fleet? It was permitted. He came nearer. He was brought before Xerxes. Yet the latter received such messengers with caution, surrounded by a wall of Immortals. The tutor, encircled by guards, began to speak:

"King of Kings! Themistocles means well by your Majesty. He wishes you to be victorious. He hopes that the allies may be destroyed. They are discussing, full of despair because you are drawing near, strong as Fate herself, whether they had not better flee and abandon the waters of Salamis."

"The narrow strait yonder?" asked Xerxes, pointing with his finger.

"You have said, Median Majesty! Attack at once, tomorrow, early in the morning. Unforgettable will be your triumph over the allies, who are at odds among themselves and continually at swords' points."

Sicinnus rowed back. He reflected how strangely portentous a single word spoken by an individual may sound in the presence of multiple power. At the same time he thought of the merry play of the dolphins, that he noticed around his boat. And he thought of the reward Themistocles had promised him in case his feigned betrayal was crowned with success—much money and, later perhaps, the right to citizenship in Thespia, when the war was over.

The tutor called himself an orator, a philosopher and a good patriot to boot.

## CHAPTER XXXVI

## A SMILE IN THE NIGHT

NIGHT fell. Many Persians were shipped over to Psyttalea, the island between the mainland and Salamis, and there put ashore. The sky was filled with shining stars. The outlines of the coasts, promontories, rocks and reefs inclined toward each other in a wondrous harmony, like goblets cunningly wrought of dark lapis lazuli and amethystine crystal by divine hands to empty out the silent sea. And the sea curved and wound and spread and contracted as though in lightly curling, violet scales.

It was then—the careful rowers hardly raised the

lightly foaming water—that the eastern wing of the Persian fleet moved out from Piræus, behind the island of Psyttalea, up to the promontory of Cynosura. The silver streams of water trickled down the oars in an ever-even rhythm, almost Lydian in suggestion, as though all this had nothing to do with the war. A voiceless silence swallowed the whispered commands. After this naval manœuvre so full of charm, which only the stars had seen, the strait of Salamis was closed on the east. The other Persian triremes drove in as close formation as possible along the coast and into the strait, doing their best to keep out of sight of the Greek ships that lay everywhere along their course. They moved on with marvelous lightness and rapidity, like some image of music and rhythm, born of the night, the silence and the beauty of that dusky-blue, ocean-violet landscape, with its amethystine, star-glittering rocks and reefs fading more and more into vaguest outline.

The little Greek fleet which had still thought to flee that morning, lay hemmed in between the two great wings of the Persian armada.

Themistocles, on look-out upon his ship, stared into the crystalline quiet of the blue night and tried to discover what had happened as a result of his cunningly feigned treason. He smiled.

## CHAPTER XXXVII

## BATTLE-DAWN

IN SALAMIS, while the dawn was still grey, the greater and lesser captains of the fleet were again gathered in consultation. Themistocles smiled; he almost mocked them as he spoke. He knew that in view of what had happened flight was no longer possible, and allowed those who still thought so to hug their delusion. At the door of the council-chamber a voice called out to him:

"Themistocles!"

He looked around. It was his enemy Aristides, son of Lysimachus, the Athenian whom the people

had banished by ostracism. He had come from
Ægina.

"What do you wish?" asked Themistocles
haughtily.

"To speak with you in private."

Themistocles followed him from the hall.

"You hate me," said Aristides.

"Yes," said Themistocles, "I hate you. Everyone praises you, although you have been banished."

"Let us forget the rancour we bear each other,"
said Aristides. "At present there is neither time
nor place for personal differences. In these days Fate
weighs heavily on Athens. The Peloponnesians
intend to flee."

"Yes," said Themistocles.

"They cannot. The Persian fleet has surrounded
us. Eurybiades and the Corinthians could not leave
these waters even though they wished. I, who am
but now come from Ægina, have seen it with my
own eyes. Go back into the council hall and tell
them. I, who am an outlaw, cannot do so."

"I had anticipated the news you give me."

"You had anticipated it?"

"Yes. The Persians have taken the advice I gave
them. I was guilty of a seeming treachery to compel
us to fight a naval battle. You have seen what I
desired: that the Persian fleet has surrounded our
own. Inform the council of it yourself. It is the
best news an expatriate can bring them. If I were
to tell them they would think I had invented it.
Walk in! If they believe you, well and good. If
they do not believe you, it is just as well. For if
we are surrounded we cannot flee."

Aristides entered the council chamber. He said:

"Athenians! With my own eyes I have seen . . ."

[179]

The fleet captains still doubted. Yet a trireme, commanded by Panaitus, had come from Tenos. He confirmed Aristides' words. Thereupon Themistocles haughtily remarked:

"This is my doing!"

It was useless to think further of flight. The captains assembled their men. Themistocles made his Athenians a long speech full of the thirst for glory. The fighting-men went aboard the galleys. The Greek fleet—three hundred sail—weighed anchor.

The sun rose, radiant and golden, as the wooden wall commenced to move. The women and children stood on the shore walls of the harbour and waved kerchiefs and veils after the defenders of the land of the Hellenic gods.

In the rosy mist of the first eastern sun-rays the tremendous Persian armada was revealed. It covered the entire horizon. It was the day of Salamis, it was the sun of Salamis. In the kindling flood of this sun's rays, invisible to mortal eyes, thronged the immortal Nikes, the victory goddesses, who wing their way from the hand of Zeus to mortal men, now to this one, now to that, as the god in his wisdom may ordain.

## CHAPTER XXXVIII

## SALAMIS

NORTHWEST of Piræus a square peninsula towers far out into the sea like a rocky seat. The placid summer waves beat melodiously against it with foamy crests. Hundreds and hundreds of years ago Nature had fashioned this spot for the sole purpose of allowing Xerxes, in his day, to throne thereon and watch the battle of Salamis.

Here the King of Kings was seated at though to witness a dramatic performance, a sham naval battle. It was a magnificent day in midsummer. The rising sun was behind Xerxes, yet he did not find it annoying, because a grateful breeze was blowing. Above the throne had been stretched a baldachin of cloth of gold. Xerxes sat there, clad in golden armour, and wearing on his head a new diadem with a pointed top. His blue-black beard was fragrant with sweet-smelling essences. He looked about him with content and condescension.

The Immortals, with Hydarnes, had been posted on all four sides of the peninsula—a wall of golden shields, spears and helmets.

Beside Xerxes was seated Mardonius, and around him many brothers, brothers-in-law and nephews. It was a radiant gathering of princes, all shining and glittering in golden armlets and chains of honour. When the sunbeams fell on them they dazzled the eye. There was a ceaseless sparkle and brilliancy. Xerxes, when he glanced about him with condescending amiability, enjoyed this uninterrupted irradiance and sparkle. He was content. And yet he mourned his two brothers, Abrocomes and Hyperanthes, who had fallen at Thermopylæ. For Xerxes had a weakness for the members of his own family, and loved his many brothers, brothers-in-law and nephews.

He also gave a passing thought to the fact that the court jeweller, who had accompanied him to Europe, had made his new diadem a trifle too big, and that the crown which Leonidas had torn from his brow at Thermopylæ had been a decidedly better fit around the sides of his head. He tried, without touching it, to shove the diadem up a bit, by wrinkling his forehead. Yet all in vain. The diadem dropped down again over his brows. Once, with graceful negligence, he thrust the crown up with his hand. When it again dropped as before, he resigned himself with philosophical indifference.

[182]

In general he felt sure of himself, calm, admirably poised on this day. The weather was wonderful, and the sight of his enormous fleet, which lay before him in a gigantic, boundless line, pointing in a north-westerly direction—both wings surrounding the Greeks—an armada which stretched from east to west, filled him with a swelling pride. He was conscious of the fact that no prince in the world had ever assembled so great an armada, backed up by so vast a host on the plains of Attica, as he, Xerxes, the King of Kings.

And he determined that he would no longer allow an ill-fitting diadem to spoil his mood. Also, he would control himself if, during the day, now and again, while he looked on, something happened that might be considered a mishap or a disaster. It might well be that some ship would fail to do its duty even though he, Xerxes, was sitting there. And he would not once leap up from his throne. He had allowed himself to be carried away, and leaped up from his field-throne when compelled to witness the accursed resistance offered his troops at Thermopylæ. But this naval throne was roomier, and more comfortable to sit on, and, all in all, Xerxes was in the best of humour and sure of victory. The god of the Persians would aid him and his.

Xerxes already had been seated on his throne for three-quarters of an hour. Now and again he spoke to Mardonius. It looked as though the King of Kings had appeared at too early an hour in his seat at the theatre to watch the play. The glittering brothers, brothers-in-law and nephews talked only in whispers, conforming to the rules of court etiquette. The Immortals stood motionless, like golden statues, gigantic, magnificent. torsos, drilled as no

Immortals elsewhere ever had been drilled. Their golden backs, their gilded shields, and their gilded helmets turned them into a golden wall, and the whole peninsula lay sparkling in the sun like one mass of gold.

Suddenly the king saw the Greek fleet draw near out of the west. All the Persians saw the Greek fleet. It rose up between the two mighty wings of the tremendous Persian armada like a small sickle. Xerxes shook his head slightly in surprise, and then reflected that he must not do so again because of his overlarge diadem. Yet his surprise was genuine. What did these Greeks imagine they were?

"It is about to start," said Xerxes.

And to an officer on duty beside him he remarked: "Send for my scribes."

The royal scribes approached, crawling on their bellies. Six of them crouched down behind Xerxes, each with long roll and stylus in hand. They were to enter the detailed account of the battle in cuneiform script.

"Behold!" said Mardonius, pointing with his hand. "Behold, O King and brother-in-law!"

And Xerxes beheld. The summer light of the morning still lay like a vapour above the blue sea, above the blue sinuosities of the receding coast, above its serrated inlets, above its projecting, spume-ringed promontories. In that quivering vapour it was hard to see everything with equal clearness at so great a distance. As they gazed Xerxes and Mardonius saw that a Greek and a Persian ship had engaged. "Which ship is that?" Xerxes asked the officers who surrounded him.

They stared, but could not place it. This annoyed Xerxes, because he could not have an entry made. Each crouching scribe had his stylus poised, only waiting for the chance to fling himself on his roll of papyrus. Out yonder it was Amænias, the Athenian, who had begun the battle. It is true that the Æginetæ afterward disputed his claim to this honour. The Greeks imagined that in the sun, which dazzled them, they beheld the shadowy figure of a goddess—Pallas Athene—who encouraged them with a gesture. Many even thought they heard the goddess admonish them not to be cowards, not to turn back their prows. In an ecstasy they saw the splendid vision in all its glory, and heard its divinely melodious voice.

Xerxes and Mardonius, now that they had gradually accustomed their eyes to the light, the mist and the distance, were able to pick out the Phœnicians. They were manœuvring opposite the Athenian fleet. The Ionians were opposed to the Lacedæmonians. Messengers rowing to and fro between the two wings of the Persian fleet informed the king and the princes with regard to what was taking place out at sea.

The messengers reported. Xerxes said:

"Enter, scribes!"

Thereupon the six scribes flung themselves on their long papyrus rolls and set down the report. The six checked up each other.

"The Ionians, faithful to the King of Kings . . ."

"And Uncle Artabanus told me that I ought to distrust the Ionians," said Xerxes, smiling haughtily.

. . . "Wrest," wrote the scribes, "many ships from the Greeks."

"Write down the number," commanded Xerxes urgently.

The scribes put down—it was always understood, though never mentioned—double the number of ships reported by the messengers.

"The names of the Ionian captains?" demanded Xerxes.

"Theomestor, son of Androdamas, and Phylacus, son of Histiæus, both of Samos," reported the messengers.

The scribes wrote. Scribbling hastily they covered their long rolls with the cuneiform lettering.

"They are brave, faithful Ionians," said Xerxes, commending them. "I shall appoint Theomestor king of Samos, and grant Phylacus estates there. And I shall bestow the title *Orosanges* on them both. Besides, I shall give Theomestor four, and Phylacus two broad armlets. Set it down, scribes!"

The scribes entered the king's promised rewards beside the Persian victories. Yet behind Mardonius the ranking official of the news service whispered:

"Princely Mardonius! Not all the Ionians are faithful. Some ships, to all appearances, at once purposely set sail to join the Greeks. There are traitors among the Ionians."

"The names of their leaders?" Mardonius asked severely.

The chief of the messenger service gave them. Mardonius, frowning, whispered the news of the Ionians' treason to Xerxes.

"How is that possible?" queried Xerxes angrily. "It cannot be true."

The better to see he narrowed his eyes and peered in the direction where the Ionians were moving in the blue distance that was growing more and more clear. Hastily and angrily he addressed the scribes, who thought that he had something for them to

enter, and respectfully stretched their scrivenish heads
up to hear the King of Kings.

"No, there is nothing to enter."

In the meantime the sea-fight blazed up along the
whole length of the straits of Salamis, blazed up in
the truest sense of the word. From the ships' cata-
pults darts dipped in sulphur and oil, to which were
attached bunches of burning tow, flew hither and
yon. Here and there, on either side, a trireme was
already aflame. It hardly seemed afire in the clear,
gold and azure day, because the yellow flame was
pale, and only the smoke floated darkly upward.
The ships crashed against each other, the bronze
peak of the first piercing the flank of the second. The
rammed ship would careen.

Movable bridges for boarding were flung from
ship to ship. The soldiers in heavy armour fought
hand to hand. They tottered and fell into the sea.

Terrible weapons were the scythes, each served by
a crew of several men. These battle scythes could
swing either way. With their lightnings, now
sharply flashing in the sun, then again darkling,
they mowed high above the heads of the crews.
They seemed to fight like furious spirits of their age,
shearing through sails and riggings. They even held
their own against masts. The ships, which but a
short time before had been manoeuvring in the mist
of the slowly clearing day with a measured neatness
of delicately-drawn shadow-outlines against the blue
sky, were caught in the sweep of each other's banks
of oars. The ships of the Persian fleet, in particular, because of their great number, locked oars in
their own teeming squadrons. The Persian rowers
cursed and swore.

Meanwhile the battle had grown hotter. While

scythes mowed, cutting and tearing tackle and sails, while masts crashed in splinters, and various ships on either side flamed up with that evanescent saffron glow at which seemed unable to take on a ruddier tinge amid all the azure and sun-gold of the summer day, the booming battering rams swayed to and fro on the chains by which they swung from the masts. Back and forth, back and forth they beat with their heavy iron spikes against the planks of the ramming ships, splintering the decks, until they capsized and sank. The awful rumbling of these battering rams, clattering and panting on their chains, became the theme song of the battle, rhythming it to the accompaniment of the roaring soldier choruses, the commands shouted in even louder tones.

From Xerxes' throne, which towered majestically above the fight, everything was visible as an indeterminate medley. And because of this jumble and confusion all could not be clearly made out. The impression produced by the naval battle was that of a tremendous two-sided chaos, a chaos which made destruction ever more apparent, while, on the other hand, every ship that went up in flames smudged out, with its grey and black smoke, what the Persian princes had but that moment clearly seen.

For a time Xerxes had not spoken. Yet—in spite of the chaos on both sides, in spite of the crowded groups of battling triremes—it became increasingly evident that the Persian fleet was suffering severe losses. The six scribes, stylus in hand, were no longer making entries. They never entered Persian ships that sank or were burned. Already, as far as Xerxes' eye could reach, the entire strait between the ships was sown with wrecks, the drifting flotsam of mowed-off rigging and sails, and drowning seamen and soldiers. And Xerxes noticed that, whereas the Greek shipwrecked all swam to Salamis, the Persians, weighed down by too heavy armour or unable to swim, drowned in thick clusters, the men gripping each other in their death agony.

Now the sky as well as the water seemed to be defiled. The lovely purity of the summer day appeared to have vanished; it showed soiled and bloated in the thick clouds that rose from the burning ships. The rocks no longer gave off a blue reflection as before, the landscape faded out in paler tints. It was almost impossible to breathe. High above Xerxes' throne whirled the burning particles, floated the smoke-blackened atoms, showered down the flakes of soot.

On the sullied waters the bravest on either side ventured out in auxiliary boats to sever the ropes of the great rudders with double-axes. This put a ship out of commission and made it incapable of manœuvring, and it was then conquered, after a sanguinary struggle on the movable bridges which the boarders flung from the one to the other deck.

Xerxes grew pale. For he saw that it was notably the ships of Persia and of her allies that were set afire, were boarded by means of long harpoons and grappling irons, and sent to the bottom by the rumbling, swaying battering rams.

Xerxes grew pale. How was it that this naval battle, whose success he thought he could have guaranteed, again did not fully satisfy his expectations? Were the Greeks really better seamen? In any event, they could swim, and the Persians and their allies could not. How is it possible that they are unable to swim? thought Xerxes. And he choked with rage because they could not swim, and because they drowned in multitudes before his eyes, whereas the Greeks, wherever he looked, calmly swam off to Salamis. His uneasiness grew more and more pronounced. He was unable longer to keep silence. Clutching the arm of Mardonius, he said in hollow tones:

"Mardonius!"

That was all he said. He saw that Mardonius was as pale as himself, that he felt as he did. He cast a swift glance around and noticed that his glittering brothers, brothers-in-law and nephews sat staring before them, pale and attentive. And finally he managed to hiss out the words:

"How pitifully they fight, and that under my very eyes! As for Achæmenes, I shall . . ."

Yet he did not say what he had in store for Achæmenes, his brother, high admiral of the fleet, on his splendid Sidonian flagship. He had suddenly risen, in spite of all his resolutions to control himself and remain seated on his throne, no matter what happened. For he had caught sight of the trireme of Artemisia, Queen of Halicarnassus, in the very thick of the jumble of ships assaulting each other with their battering rams. Her tattered sails were flaming. An Athenian trireme was pursuing her. She fled with a dip and bend of panting oars until she reached some ships of her own party. Then she did not hesitate a moment. The trireme of the Queen of Halicarnassus struck the ship of Damasythimus, King of the Calyndians, Persia's ally, which lay across her course, square in the flank with its pointed prow.

The rammed ship sank as though drawn under water. Artemisia's trireme sped on, swerving almost imperceptibly.

The Athenian, thinking he had made a mistake, and that Artemisia's ship was friendly to the Greeks, tacked about and made off on another course.

"Who was it Artemesia rammed and sank?" Xerxes asked.

It was known among his entourage that he was well-disposed toward her. No one—even though they might have recognized him—thought much of the Calyndians and Damasythimus, their unimportant, two-penny king. It was a question whether any member of his crew would survive to report what had happened. It seemed as though a sudden, secret conspiracy in favour of Artemisia had come into being. At the critical moment Xerxes was not thinking of Damasythimus, was hardly aware of his ally's existence. There must have been an odd hundred or so of these kinglets. Did Xerxes, the King of Kings, know the whole hundred of these petty monarchs?

"King of Kings!" rang the cry of those about Xerxes. "Artemisia is the bravest fighter, for all she is a woman! Did you see how she rammed and sank the Athenian vessel?"

"Was it an Athenian?" asked Xerxes.

"It was an Athenian! It was an Athenian!" cried the nephews and brothers-in-law. Mardonius, uncertain of his ground, kept silence.

"That woman fights like a man," said Xerxes, "whereas my men . . ."

He would have liked to add: "fight like women." But he controlled himself. He did not say so, but called out to the scribes who rushed up:

"Enter, scribes! Artemisia, Queen of Halicarnassus, Cos and Nisyrus, rams and sinks an Athenian trireme. Take pride in the fact that it is your privilege to enter this event!"

A messenger had stepped ashore from a boat at the base of the crag on which stood the throne. He clambered up the steps hewn out of the rock. Staggering, despairing, helmetless, he flung himself at Xerxes' feet and cried:

"Lord! King of Kings! The son of Darius, Ariabignes, your royal brother and admiral of the fleet, has drowned. His ship has been rammed and sunk with all its officers and crew."

"What?" shouted Xerxes in a fury.

A second messenger followed the first. Heavily wounded, bleeding, he cast himself at Xerxes' feet and panted:

"Lord! I have to report that owing to the treachery of the Ionians, the miserable Ionians, the Phœnician ships have been destroyed."

"The Ionians! The Ionians!" roared Xerxes, clenching his fists. "They are traitors. Uncle Artabanus warned us!"

A third messenger flung himself down before the throne, while the scribes in their perplexity knew not what to enter nor how to enter it.

"King of Kings! I have to report to the contrary, that the Samothracian Ionians have rammed and sunk an Athenian trireme."

"Enter the victory!" Xerxes bade the scribes. Again they flew to their task and covered their rolls of papyrus with hastily scribbled cuneiform characters.

The second messenger had fallen to the ground and was carried away by his two comrades. A fourth messenger, dripping water, flung himself at full length before Xerxes' throne:

[192]

"Lord! King of Kings! An Æginetan trireme has sunk the Samothracian ship about which my predecessor reported."

Xerxes ground his teeth with rage, he clenched his fists. The messengers succeeded each other, they formed an ascending line on the stairs hewn in the rock. Even the round, motionless, golden backs of the Immortals betrayed a quiver of movement.

One after another the messengers cast themselves at Xerxes' feet. If one brought good news the next discounted it. It was increasingly evident that it would no longer be possible to win the naval battle, incredible though that might seem.

In turn Xerxes made every commander and every nation responsible for the fact that the battle was not progressing as he wished. Yet at the same time he was filled with increasing astonishment to think that the clumsy little Athenian ships not only held their own against his overwhelming armada, but even threatened to destroy it. It was incredible, incredible, and yet he saw it happening as he sat on his throne.

In the meantime, the Samothracians, for all their ship was sinking, had boarded the Æginetan trireme which had attacked them, had taken possession of it and—admirable javelin-throwers that they were— had driven off and slain its crew. This heroic deed made Xerxes feel somewhat better, and distracted his attention from the Ionians, those traitors against whom Uncle Artabanus had warned him. Yet since his rage had to have some outlet, it turned on the Phœnicians, whose ships had been destroyed.

"See that all the Phœnician captains who have saved themselves are beheaded!" roared Xerxes, his eyes drunken with anger, the overlarge diadem hang-

[193]

ing slantwise over his forehead, "so that these cowards will be unable to defame men who were braver than they."

At this moment, with one excitement succeeding another, the Ionians were saved. On the fouled water, through the sullied air, it was clearly evident that the afflicted Persian fleet, in its bewilderment, was attempting a retreat behind the island of Psyttalea into the bay of Phaleron. The Persian fleet was in flight. On the rocky plateau where stood Xerxes' throne, all the princes, as well as Mardonius, had risen and were watching the flight of the Persian armada. The Athenian vessels were pursuing, and the Ægean ships boldly rowed to meet it. It fell as though into a trap, entangling itself in its own all too numerous, too closely-crowding banks of oars. The sailors cursed. The defeat was visible, was even audible. It was past all doubt.

"Xerxes," whispered Mardonius, forgetting all courtier reticences, "it is no longer safe up here!"

On the island of Psyttalea itself, where thousands of Persians were attempting to land, the battle raged, almost directly in front of Xerxes' throne. Aristides, Themistocles' enemy (but reconciled to him during these days), with a band of Athenian hoplites devoted to him, destroyed the Persians.

With a single despairing glance, Xerxes embraced the whole smoke-blackened landscape of the straits of Salamis. The coasts, dissolving more and more in the black and grey of the burning vessels, the promontories, the cliffs, whose erstwhile blue and delicately hazy sky line he could no longer recognize, transformed as it now was into a fiendish landscape of tribulation, while rudders, wreckage and corpses were cast up on the rocks by the swelling

[194]

tide.   Then he said to Mardonius no more than the one word:

"Come!"

All the Persian backs on the rocky eminence turned around, those of the Immortals, the nephews, brothers-in-law and brothers, that of Xerxes himself.   They showed as a ceaseless glitter, a line of vain gold, its sparkle slowly fading in the setting sun, a glitter which, as though ashamed, flowed down the stairs hewn in the stone.   The King of Kings was in flight.

## CHAPTER XXXIX

## THE POET'S VISION

NIGHT spread with a strange serenity over the level sea on which the naval battle had rolled and raged that day. A man had slowly clambered up the cliff. North of Salamis, high up on the rocks, he wearily seated himself and stared before him. There was no sign of the vanquished Persian fleet from this point. It had retreated in a southeasterly direction, into the bay of Phaleron.

The man could see the Greek fleet—a small curved sickle, as it had appeared the preceding day—lying off Salamis. There was nothing, at night, to betray the damage it had suffered. Only here and there a sail or a mast was missing from one of these ships that seemed to lie side by side in a state of exhaustion. The smoke and fumes of the fires had not yet fully disappeared. A smell of burning was still noticeable. The stars pushed their way through a mist growing increasingly lighter.

The weary man, as he looked about him, gradually accustomed himself to the darkness and was able to recognize more and more. To the north he could make out the breadth of the Eleusinian bight. It lay like the ocean, without a horizon, hardly moving in the calm. Then, increasingly plain to his sight, he recognized, fronting him, the tremendous ridges of the Ægaleonian mountains against the nocturnal sky, in which a growing number of stars had begun to twinkle. The outlines of the coasts and the points of the promontories stood out stratawise in vague violet outlines, like the wings of some world-wide, ethereal stage.

The man rested his elbow on his knee, cupped his chin in his palm, and dreamily allowed his glance to range over the incredible quiet and breadth that had succeeded upon so much unrest and savagery. Not a sound came to him, either from the town below, whither the Athenians had returned to their wives and children, mindful of their dead as well as of their victory, nor from the fleet, on whose decks the crews slept the sleep of exhaustion.

The dream of the man in that violet night, in the vast reaches of silence and solitude, turned into a dream of fate and of the gods, of wrongdoing and of pity, and it seemed to him, as though between these wings, so like those of a celestial stage, the shades of his dream rose up before his eyes.

The man was Æschylus, son of Euphorion, born in Eleusis. He had that day fought against the Persians aboard an Athenian trireme. He had fought beside his brother Amænias. Ten years before he had fought at Marathon beside his brother Cynægirus, who had had an arm chopped off and had died there. But Æschylus was not only a brave, fighting sailor of the Athenian fleet, he was a poet as well. For the past twenty years he had been writing his tragedies, and together with the famous Pratinas he had contested for the laurel wreath in the poetic competitions. Many times had he been crowned with it.

He had been the first who had staged dramas in accordance with his own ideas, in the new stone theatre of Dionysus, erected on the site of the old wooden building on the southern slope of the Athenian Acropolis. For the day of the Thespian chariots, on which Bacchic dithyrambs were sung by actors rouged with wine lees, was over. That had represented unfettered art's inspiration of the moment. It had been no studied declamation, but an art lovely, simple and natural, welling up out of the ecstasied hearts of its poet-actors, who had vocalized religion and tragedy in an uncontrollable cry of rapture. And then they had wandered on with their donkey-drawn cart through the towns and past the villages like carefree strollers, enjoying life, and delighting in the beauty they sensed within themselves and bestowed in ever-flowing abundance for the few coins they begged, or often for no more than a meal.

When Æschylus, the poet-warrior, thought of that day of first attempts, melancholy well-nigh overcame him, and he was conscious of the mutations of fate. And indeed, in his restlessly active imagination

[198]

he was ever conscious of the governance of destiny. Ever before him rose the shades of the mighty. He saw them yonder between the dusky hills, gliding by in the violet night, and on the slopes of the distant mountains. He saw them striding along on their high buskins, figures superhuman, heroic, divine, with the spacious gesture of their wide-sleeved arms, the splendid folds of their ornate mantles, and with the lofty expression—inspiring dread and awe—of their great masks. It seemed to him that he could hear the heavily tragic outpouring of their insistent prayers sound forth in rhythmically measured speech from the mouth-openings of their masks. He seemed to hear them while above him, in that night of radiant stars, the gods determined the joys and woes of mortals, and round about them the goddesses of destiny, the unescapable ones, and all-powerful, inexorable, omnipresent Fate herself reigned supreme in a terrifying omnipotence that led one to pity the inevitable suffering that mortals must endure, and the wrongs because of which they suffer, wrongs which the interlocking chain of their deeds makes them unable to avoid. It was an omnipotence which made mortals recognize in their wrongdoing a fated guilt, in view of which all that remained was to show themselves devout and humble when confronted with this irresistible power.

Thus the poet-warrior, as he dreamed there in the night, saw the mighty shades. He saw the shade of Agamemnon and of Clytemnestra. He saw the shade of Prometheus between the floating Oceanidæ, come to console him. He saw the shade of Orestes between the pursuing Eumenides. He saw the exalted malefactors and the glorified gods who decreed their fate, while the fates of individuals

[199]

seemed to merge into one monstrous destiny, filling the whole night sky beyond and between the stars, and within the compass of all that the mind can grasp and conceive, and even further, past the limits of world and planets.

Suddenly the warrior-poet, the dreamer-poet Æschylus, in the irresistibly thronging imaginative world of his fantasy, saw the reality of the past day itself. As though in a lofty apotheosis he beheld all that had occurred that day in the narrows of the straits of Salamis: the destruction of the gigantic Persian armada, in which he himself had participated as an individual out of love for country, though he was no longer young. Above all, he saw what, beheld from the deck of his own Athenian trireme, had made a tremendous impression on him, the flight —in a golden, glittering line that faded out in the setting sun—of the King of Persia and all those who had surrounded him with their radiance.

See, over yonder! There, between the violet-tinted promontories and the amethystine islands radiant in the starlight, they are teeming once more. Yet the sight is loftier, more tremendous, more awe-inspiring, perhaps, than it was in reality, and devoid of the irony which always clings to the actual. They are teeming once more.

It seemed to Æschylus as though some of his own patriotism lost itself in this subconsciously greater, universally human surge of compassion which over-powered his poet's soul, after the horror with which his sense of human guilt had caused it to shudder. He pitied the guilt of Xerxes, the arrogance of his monstrous crime, that had mercilessly and inde-fatigably dragged along millions and had sacrificed them to what the man fancying he was God had

[200]

striven for in order to realize his unrealizable, vainglorious and immortal thought—to weigh earthly omnipotence in his feeble hands. This he wished to do though the omnipotence of heaven, wherein earthly omnipotence is whirled about like a thread in a whirlpool, outweighs all humanity and crushes all that is not humble.

It was a strange, monstrous pity felt by this Greek who had that day fought for his country with all the courage and with all the reserves of strength on which he could draw. It was an inexplicable, a divine pity felt by this Athenian poet, who forgot that he was a soldier. He compassionated that Persian king whom, like a malefactor, like a felon, he had seen turn his back in flight over yonder on the rock, beside his throne, in the midst of his people.

It was a flight back into that far distance whence he had come, to Persia, to the land out of which he had marched with millions of warriors, with countless peoples and countless kings, with numberless relatives of the blood royal, haughty and sure of victory, across bridged seas and severed mountains! It was an inconceivable, unspeakable pity that surged in Æschylus' breast, despite his creative brain, and that flowed rhythmically from his lips in winged verses! How he pitied Xerxes, the arrogant, broken, monstrous, fugitive Xerxes! He saw him yonder in the violet landscape fleeing from the rock and the sea. He saw him stalking in high buskins, wringing hands which projected from the broad royal mantle he had torn in his despair. He saw him lamenting his vanquished warriors from the rounded hollow of his mask-mouth, as the features of his tragic mask showed horribly distorted in the gleam of the violet-tinted mists of night!

Yonder, over yonder, hidden by the mists, lay the unknown land of dreams, Persia; lay the princely city, Susa. There echoed the rounded tones of those sonorously ringing Persian names: Ariomardus, Pharandakes, Hystaichmes, Anchares, Xanthis, Arsames, which seemed to rend the night like bitter lamentations as the faithful Elders in Susa called on Xerxes to tell them what he had done with so many brave, splendidly blooming young brothers, brothers-in-law and nephews. And Xerxes, out yonder on that far-flung nocturnal stage, called back that they had fallen, and had been left on the battle-field. He cried that their corpses were drifting on the sea amidst thousands of shattered oars, that their bodies would be washed up on the savage, rocky enemy coasts, and would never be honourably laid on the funeral pyre. And he cried to the Elders:

"Weep and wail, lament and sob as I do! Tear your garments, ye Elders! Pluck out your hair and beard! Hear the whole tale of our misfortune. They have all perished! All of them are dead! Behold! I have brought back my quiver, but it no longer holds a single arrow! I have been despoiled of my arms! I have torn my royal mantle! I have lost my crown! My Immortals were only mortal!"

And the faithful Elders responded:

"The might of Persia is broken! Our sorrow is more than we can bear! We beat our breasts! Loud are our sobs and lamentations! We grieve and we despair!"

"Raise the mystic song of lamentation!" cried the shade of Xerxes from the shadows.

And the Elders cried:

'Shall we show ourselves to the people in our despair?"

"Yes!" answered Xerxes, in his anguish. "Persia shall bear witness to my despair, to our despair! Woe is me! I have lost my ships! Mourn, ye Persians, who once were so happy!"

After this outburst of sorrow, it seemed to the poet—in whom the pity which flooded his soul momentarily extinguished the warrior, and even all sense of patriotism, so that he was a poet only—that the form of a mother rose before his eyes. He saw Atossa. She did not appear to him as an oriental princess, seated on a couch, whip in hand, about to chastise her slaves and laundresses, amid the cloying steam of cooking fruits and attar of roses. He saw her in imposing relief, clarified, spiritualized, between the transparent violet hills, beyond which the palace of Susa vaguely shimmered. He saw her grown divinely great in her regal and maternal dignity.

She advanced in the robes of tragedy, wringing her hands, filled with cares and dreams uncomprehended, which she begged the wise Elders to interpret. And at last—as a messenger brought her the lamentable tidings—he saw her fling up her maternal arms, and through the black distended orifice of her mask-mouth shriek aloud because of her son, the divine Xerxes, who with torn mantle and empty quiver was fleeing back across the bridged seas and the channelled mountains.

And while the poet's soul overflowed in horror and pity there on that high lonely rock, towering over Salamis and granting a view of Eleusis, Æschylus' *The Persians* was conceived in his creative imagination and in his quivering emotion with that sacred, convulsive joy that blesses conception in the poet.

## CHAPTER XL

## MARDONIUS' OATH

IN HIS haxamaxa, heavily curtained, its four horses running furiously, Xerxes fled back to Athens. He was surrounded only by an escort of Immortals, the rest of the army and the princes following after. Not a Persian had as yet uttered the word "flight," but rage and terror spoke in every waving fold of the soldier mantles which fluttered from the shoulders of the horsemen. As Xerxes lay relaxed in his carriage, rumbling along the road to Athens, he asked himself: How could it have happened? Had his armada actually been defeated by those clumsy Greek ships? Already he had ceased calling them "little" ships. With a child's incredulity he asked himself the question a thousand times, while he lay stretched out uncomfortably in all his armour, holding his ill-fitting diadem in his hand.

As a matter of fact, it was a flight, though not the splendidly tragic flight the creative imagination of the poet-warrior had that night evoked. For Xerxes did not tear his garments, nor pluck out his hair. The King of Kings had slung across his shoulder no quiver such as Æschylus had beheld symbolically void of arrows. The King of Kings was too exalted to be his own bowman.

After the return to Athens, to that house which, no doubt, had been metamorphosed into a Persian palace, the princes and generals were all on tenterhooks. What decision would be reached? Suddenly Xerxes appeared, and in a shrill voice, trembling with rage, commanded:

"Give orders that the mainland and that accursed Salamis be at once joined together!"

The princes and the generals stood as though petrified, staring uncomprehendingly, with wide-open mouths.

"I mean," Xerxes continued, furious, "that you are to have the Phœnician freighters roped together to form a bridge, a wall. Then we shall still get the better of the Greeks."

He clenched his fists and shut himself up in his chamber.

There he sat, staring before him, and wondering how he was to send the news of that ill-omened day to Susa. Should he write Uncle Artabanus? Atossa? He saw no way out.

Mardonius begged for an interview. Xerxes

lacked courage to refuse it to his brother-in-law and captain-general. He was allowed to enter.

"What do you wish?" Xerxes roughly asked him.

Mardonius, very pale, stood before the King of Kings who, seated on his throne, continued to stare into space, devoid of counsel and inwardly raging. Mardonius, who felt that he was to blame for their misfortunes, for the whole war, which he had forced through, spoke:

"Xerxes, my lord and brother-in-law! Tell me —we are alone—do you in truth mean to chance another naval battle? Or is this bridge at Salamis a trick which I, at least, can divine, to prepare a general flight and let us get the start of the pursuing Greeks?"

"I don't know," replied Xerxes, his eyes rolling wildly. "I no longer know anything."

Then Mardonius spoke with deep emotion. For Mardonius had a noble soul, for all that he had advised the war:

"O King! Cease to mourn what has happened at Salamis! No longer consider it an irremediable evil. The success of this war does not depend on our ships alone. Is not Mardonius left you? Have you not still your whole tremendous army on land, its foot-men and its horsemen? Has that ever been excelled? Has it ever been equalled? The Greeks, who may imagine they have gained all, will not leave their ships, on whose decks alone they are strong, to fight against us. Those who have remained ashore are worthless.

'My King, now put your faith in Mardonius! We will at once storm the Peloponnesus! Or do you prefer to pause for rest? We shall not lose heart if you do. The Greeks are exhausted; they shall yet be your slaves. The time will come when you will call them to account both for the present and for the past. The time will come when you will call them to account for Marathon and for Salamis. Yet should you prefer, as I suspect, to return to Persia, then listen to my counsel, O King!"

Mardonius was deeply moved. It is true that his noble soul could not see what the future was to bring forth, but he was deeply moved. He knelt on one knee before Xerxes, who sat there, still furious and at his wits' end, and said:

"Do not suffer us, O King, to become a mock for these Greeks! The Persians have done your cause no despite. The Persians have fought like lions. It is our cowardly allies who are guilty. The Phœnicians, the Egyptians, the Cyprians and the Cilicians failed to do their duty. For their deeds we, and I, Xerxes, are not to blame! Believe what I tell you, Xerxes!"

Mardonius dared seize the hand of his brother-in-law, and continue:

"If you do not wish to remain, then return with the greater part of the host, and leave me here with no more than three hundred thousand men. I swear to you by our gods that I shall either make the Greeks bow beneath the yoke of your power, or die."

Xerxes, too, was deeply moved. He looked long at Mardonius, admiring his noble soul. Xerxes was conquered by the splendid dramatism of the moment. For Xerxes was prone to æsthetic impulses. That, too, which the poet-warrior was in process of shaping in verse respecting Xerxes would have made a deep impression on the King of Kings. Xerxes would have admired Æschylus' *The Persians*, if the chance to hear and see the tragedy which dealt with his own fate had ever been vouchsafed him. Overcome by his emotion and yielding to an impulse of tenderness, Xerxes opened his arms. He did so with a dramatic gesture, it may be quite unconsciously. Yet, however he did it, it was well done. He embraced Mardonius, still kneeling, drew him to him, and said:

"Mardonius! You are a hero and you have a noble soul!"

Then Mardonius turned soberly business-like after his emotional excess, and said:

"Let us take counsel with our brothers, brothers-in-law and nephews, as to what remains to be done."

Xerxes agreed. The meeting was called. After Xerxes had consulted with his brothers, nephews and brothers-in-law—he already had glanced several times around the hall filled with so many generals—he said:

"Where is the Queen of Halicarnassus? Why is Artemisia not here? Send for the Queen of Halicarnassus! She is a heroine, and I attach the greatest importance to hearing what she may advise me to do."

Artemisia, who had been listening behind a curtain, somewhat uneasy because of the trireme of her friends the Calyndians and of their king, Damasithymus, which she had holed as a measure of self-preservation, at once entered, her heart beating loudly beneath her cuirass. Xerxes remained alone with Artemisia. For he wished to hear her without witnesses. The brothers, brothers-in-law and nephews felt offended thereat, but did not show it.

They went. Xerxes motioned the queen to a seat. He said:

"Artemisia! Mardonius advises me to storm the

[208]

Peloponnesus, or to return to Persia with my army, and leave him in Attica with three hundred thousand men to force the Greeks beneath my yoke. You, Artemisia, who but yesterday proved yourself a heroine . . ."

Artemisia breathed more freely. Xerxes knew nothing.

"Tell me, what would you advise me to do?"

"O King!" jubilantly cried the triumphant woman. Then she artfully lowered her joyous voice.

"It is difficult to advise you in this matter. Yet I am of the opinion we should go, and that you should leave Mardonius behind with the troops he may select. He says he will force the Greeks beneath your yoke . . ."

She rose. Swiftly she gazed about her. Then she seated herself on the steps of Xerxes' throne and whispered up to him:

"If he is successful, yours will be the credit, Xerxes! If he does not succeed it makes no difference. You will be far away and in safety. You, together with all your princely house. So long as Xerxes lives the Greeks will tremble, even though chance favours them today. You will fight them again and again, and sooner or later you will crush them. The time will come when they will bow their necks. And if Mardonius falls, what is he save a slave of Xerxes, as all of us, O Prince, are your slaves?"

Seductively she raised her face and looked at him. She was beautiful, and he could not elude the picturesque, almost mythical charm this sea-amazon exerted. She was a heroine and yet very woman. What he had not tolerated at his own court, what he

[209]

had found contradictory to the traditions of the harem in Susa, seemed most attractive to him while in the field. This royal combatant, who acted as though she loved him, while he acted as though he loved her, was a diversion, at that moment, an embellishment of life and very necessary to him. This Semiramis, who crouched so cajolingly at his feet, in the mail that covered her bosom, the greaves that sheathed her legs, enchanted him. She merged harmoniously with his mood of the moment. One of his concubines—they accompanied him in great numbers—in her long, dragging Median woman's gown, would have made hardly any impression on him at that instant.

"Artemisia!" he began tenderly.

She leaned questioningly against his knee. His blue-black beard tickled her forehead. But a sudden new excitement awoke in Xerxes. He thought of his three young bastard sons, of whom he was passionately fond, and who had accompanied him.

"Artemisia," Xerxes went on, in another tone, "I thank you for your advice, I thank you for the love you have shown me. Yet the moment is not propitious for . . . I have too much on my mind. I am thinking of my three sons. I tremble for them. They are young and my sole joy. They may even now be in danger. Who knows with what difficulties the retreat may yet be attended? Can I entrust them to you, Artemisia? Surely you will be able to sally out unobserved with your ship and take them to Ephesus?"

Artemesia rejoiced inwardly. She infinitely preferred this confidence to a lover's hour spent with the king. She had nothing further to fear, and at once agreed.

Xerxes gave an order to the guard:

"Have the little princes brought in!"

The three bastard princes entered. They were three handsome little Persian boys, with amber-yellow complexions and black curls, and richly adorned. With their jewelled amulets and their little jewelled daggers, they seemed toys with which Xerxes played. When the eunuch Hermotimus led them in their father embraced them with great tenderness.

Behind them there was pushing and shoving, and the officer on duty at the door bowed to earth and cried:

"The royal mail, O King of Kings!"

The courier brought letters from Susa. It was the splendidly managed Persian postal service. It was the courier who had come trotting from the last postal station, where he had in all haste taken over from his predecessor the letters for Xerxes and his brothers, brothers-in-law and nephews. Snow, rain, heat, darkness, naught could stop the trotting Persian courier. He flung himself down full length before Xerxes' throne, and delivered his pouch with both hands.

The brothers, brothers-in-law and nephews, who had been informed, entered. The letters were distributed.

Xerxes had received a letter from Amestris, the queen, one from the Allhighest Mother, Atossa, one from Uncle Artabanus. They were full of rejoicing at the fall of Athens.

They read approximately the same:

"To Xerxes, King of Kings. We rejoice because our prince is master of Athens, and the lofty goal of the war has been attained. The streets of Susa are

[211]

strewn with myrtle branches, and in all the squares smoke is rising from the bowls of burning incense offered the Persian gods.  We look forward, O Xerxes, to your return in triumph!  . . ."

Xerxes had begun to read.  Pale and silent, all listened to him.  And then, suddenly, Xerxes crumpled Uncle Artabanus' papyrus into a ball and flung it to the ground.  For it was the evening of Salamis.

"Burn Athens, O King of Kings!" Artemisia cried jubilantly, as she put her arms about the three bastard princes, the three little boys, and departed.  The eunuchs followed her.

## CHAPTER XLI

## THE ANDROSIANS

THAT night, by supreme command, the remainder of the Persian fleet, together with Artemisia, withdrew from the harbour of Phaleron. The fleet steered east with all speed. In the night haze, with all sails spread, it seemed like a crowd of prodigious, ghostly, winged sea monsters, with long paws, hurrying across the water, rising from and dipping down into the waves. It was an astonishing vision, like an image, transparently clear in the radiance of the rising moon, of the vanity of human power, vain and impotent because the gods had so willed. And now it rowed, it sailed away,

[213]

to protect the bridge of ships across the Hellespont against possible attack and destruction by the Greeks. Although this was its object, the fleet seemed a fleeing horde of sea monsters rather than a fleet still powerful and able to give battle.

The silence of night kept the secret of its flight, and the pallid moonlight shrouded it with her veil of mystery. It was the fleet's mystery as well, that made her, herself a phantom, see ghosts when, in her fear, the promontories, rocks and islands emerging from the moon-mist seemed to take the form of Greek ships sailing to meet her. So that the fleet's own vessels, which seemed ghosts to the terrified islands who beheld them steer by in the night, fled hither and yon, as though driven by a wind that never blew, and then, conscious of their mistake, again assembled to melt away on the horizon and vanish to meet the security of morn.

That morning the Greeks saw the Persian land forces camp on the farther side of Salamis.

They thought the Persian fleet was still at Phaleron.

Yet soon they learned of the flight, and pursued it with their ships as far as the island of Andros. The Persian fleet, however, was no longer visible.

The Greeks held council in Andros.

"Let us pursue the Persian fleet through the Ægean Sea," cried Themistocles. "We must destroy the bridge of boats across the Hellespont."

"We must be careful not to do so," exclaimed Eurybiades. "If Xerxes cannot retreat with his millions, that greatest of misfortunes—the famine which already threatens—will be our portion."

"Let us give the king a chance to flee!" said the Peloponnesian captains.

"We will fight against him later, in his own land,"
others shouted.

Themistocles, in one of his genial impulses, had
already, in imagination, seen the Persian king shut
off from Asia and in the hands of the Athenians,
who did with him as they listed. The fancy had
a dazzling, seductive appeal.

Later Themistocles himself laughed at it.

Yet the Athenian captains surrounding Themistocles were indignant with the allies for allowing the
Persian fleet to escape. They proposed sailing to
the Hellespont without them.

It seemed as though Themistocles, smiling, had
an inkling of that future which was later to condemn
him. Out of favour in Athens? Why not, in view
of the caprices of the goddess of fortune? Ostracism? A refuge? Where? In Persia? All this in
vaguest outline rose before his mental eye. Yet it
was the subconscious divination of genius regarding
what actually was to take place.

Themistocles, still smiling, said, with a weary
gesture:

"Athenians! This would not be the first time
that a vanquished enemy were thus, in his perplexity, offered a new prospect of making up for his first
mischance. Athenians! Now that we have, contrary to our own expectations, driven off the barbarian hordes, let us not pursue a fleeing foe! We
owe our victory not to our own strength, but to the
protecting shades of our heroes and the god of the
Greeks. Our god, our mighty Zeus, would not suffer that a mere impious man, a wretched wight incapable of distinguishing the divine from the human,
should burn the temples of the gods, and cast down
their images, that he alone should be victor over

[215]

Europe and Asia. Athenians! We have gained a great advantage. Let us not seek to gain a greater! Let us remain in Hellas! Let us devote ourselves to our own! The Barbarian has been driven out. We will rebuild what he has destroyed. Let us sow the harvest of the future, and when spring comes march to the Hellespont and invade Ionia!"

The Athenians cheered Themistocles. But Themistocles at once sent the tutor Sicinnus to Xerxes with a secret message. The tutor entered a boat with a few men and was rowed along the Attic shore. He beckoned to a Persian sentry.

"I am a messenger whom the admiral of the Athenian fleet has sent to the King of the Medes."

Sicinnus was led to Athens, into the presence of Xerxes. Sicinnus noticed the excitement in the captured city.

Xerxes recognized him. This was the man who had advised him to attempt Salamis. He grew pale with rage. But the tutor said:

"Median Majesty! Themistocles, son of Neocles, high admiral of the Athenian fleet, sends me to you to let you know he is not ill-disposed to you."

"Themistocles?" queried Xerxes doubtfully.

"Positively, Median Majesty! And to tell you that you and your sons should never forget . . ."

"What . . ."

The tutor pronounced each word with oratorical emphasis:

"That to benefit you he prevented the Greeks, allies and Athenians, from pursuing your fleet and destroying the bridge across the Hellespont. You may return untroubled to your empire, Median Majesty!"

The tutor had himself rowed back. He found

Themistocles on his ship, busy counting money in his cabin. Themistocles smiled when he heard that his message to Xerxes had been delivered.

"Why you send me to the Mede on this occasion," said the tutor, "is a riddle I cannot solve."

"I'm not sure I can solve it myself," replied Themistocles uncertainly.

"Why do you practically bid for the Mede's friendship?"

"Do you think what I did was treasonable, Sicinnus?"

"The gods forbid, master, that I utter the word! It was due to your seeming treason that the Athenian fleet won the battle of Salamis. But then I understood the message I had to deliver. This time I did not. I delivered it as badly as the second lead this spring, in the theatre of Dionysus, acted in a tragedy by Æschylus, son of Euphorion."

Themistocles rose.

"Sicinnus," he said, "I need money, a great deal of money."

"You are too fond of money, master," said Sicinnus discontentedly. "Since you were a mere boy you have spent far too much money."

"That is quite possible," answered Themistocles with a laugh. "I am merely a human being, with human weaknesses. I am no Leonidas."

"What do you mean by that, master?"

"I am not a demigod and a Spartan."

"You are an Athenian."

"Yes," said Themistocles, "and a human being in need of money. Back to shore with you and tell the authorities of Andros that they must not fail to give Athens money in honour of the two great goddesses."

"Which goddesses, master!"

"Those of necessity and of persuasion," Themistocles laughingly replied.

The tutor went. An hour later he was aboard again.

"Well?" said Themistocles.

"The Androsians say, master, that Athens, protected by such powerful goddesses, is entitled to be great, rich and powerful. Yet on their island dwell only . . ."

"Who?"

"Poverty and impossibility."

"Then they refused?"

"They even added that Athens' power could never be more powerful than their inability is impotent."

Themistocles no longer smiled. He frowned and said:

"They are witty, but we will besiege them. These Androsian traitors! Sicinnus, go to Carystos and Paros! Ask for money there! I need a great deal of money."

## CHAPTER XLII

## FLIGHT

IN ATHENS preparations were under way for the retreat of the whole tremendous millionary host, which was to withdraw to Bœotia along the same route by which it had advanced. For Mardonius thought it would be wiser to accompany it part way, and to go into winter quarters with the troops he had selected, in order to march to the Peloponnesus in the spring. When Mardonius had returned to Thessaly, he picked his men. He chose the Immortals. But their leader, Hydarnes, preferred to remain with Xerxes. He chose the *Thorekophoræ*, heavily-armed, armoured infantry, and a body of a thousand horse, Medes, Sacæ, Bactrians and some Indians.

He formed picked troops of individual well-drilled soldiers who, because of deeds of valour, had been awarded many chains and armlets that hung heavily down over their cuirasses or broadly clasped their sinewy arms. When Xerxes, on that last morning, in all haste—for he was unable to rid himself of his incubus that the bridge across the Hellespont might be destroyed and the allies cut off his road of retreat to Asia—reviewed Mardonius' army of three hundred thousand picked men, his arrogance, so lately quenched, flamed up once more. It might be taken for granted that the allies would be unable to get the better of this magnificent army, even though at sea capricious Tyche—most inconceivably —had opposed the Persians.

After the review a Lacedæmonian herald was led into Xerxes' presence. How had this person managed to discover him in Thessaly? Xerxes puzzled over it with concealed anxiety, and he was unable to rid himself of the thought that the bridge of ships already might have been destroyed in spite of the message Themistocles—that unreliable Athenian— had sent him. The herald had been sent from Sparta, because of a Delphic oracle which ordered that Xerxes be called to account for the death of Leonidas, and that whatever reply the king might make be accepted as an omen.

Xerxes sat his horse proudly. His diadem now fitted him snugly. Thus he received the herald, who said:

"King of the Medes! The Lacedæmonians and the Heraclidæ of Sparta demand satisfaction of you for the death of Leonidas!"

[220]

Xerxes burst into laughter, loud and continuous. "Is that all?" he asked haughtily. "Do the Spartans send me a herald merely to hold me so vainly to account?"

At that moment Mardonius came riding up, a splendid figure at the head of his splendid staff.

With the grandiloquent gesture he had regained, Xerxes pointed out Mardonius.

"Behold, herald, there rides the hero who will give your countrymen satisfaction!"

The herald stared at Mardonius. He took in the army with a long glance. Then he said:

"I accept your word as an omen, Xerxes, as the oracle ordained."

Xerxes shrugged his shoulders. The herald went. Yet the King of Kings could not rid himself of his incubus. He bade Mardonius farewell.

This Mardonius has a noble soul, after all, Xerxes often thought during his retreat, a retreat which grew more and more terrible day by day, a retreat which resembled a continuous defeat, although no blood was shed, a defeat due to famine, plague and dysentery. Along the road and in the fields the exhausted warriors were abandoned. They fed on what little seed-grain they could discover, on the pasture grass, on the bark and leaves of wild and cultivated trees. There was not much else to be found. All had already been devoured by those same hordes when they had invaded Greece.

In all the cities through which Xerxes passed, in which penury, together with famine and sickness, ruled, he left thousands of warriors, sowing them behind him in his passage. He left behind him whole peoples, the peoples his army had erstwhile dragged along with it in an ever-increasing flood.

[221]

"Feed my soldiers and care for them!" was the order Xerxes gave the authorities in all places.

It was a vain word, a command impossible of execution. There was nothing but rain. There was, indeed, water in the rivers, in which the plague-stricken and the dysenterics could quench their thirst, but the water was poisoned. The dying lay strewn with the dead along the roadsides. Xerxes pushed on, his eyes staring into space. Ordinarily he had himself driven in his tightly-closed haxamaxa, the horses trotting their swiftest under the lash, till their knees gave way.

When he reached Macedonia he asked for the sacred chariot of the Zeus of the Persians. But the chariot had disappeared. The Pæonians had put it in charge of the Thracians. When he demanded it of the Thracians, they told Xerxes that the sacred Nisæan steeds had been stolen by the robbers of upper Thrace, who dwelt by the unattainable sources of the Strymon, and who, from their lofty cliffs, had laughed Xerxes to scorn when he had gone by in the spring.

At Eion on the Strymon Xerxes boarded a Phœnician trireme. The retreat of the army lasted five and forty days. It was a dissolution whose horror increased with every day that passed. At last the Hellespont greeted their eyes, and Hydarnes, who was leading the army, heaved a sigh of relief when he saw the bridge of ships. No matter how damaged by storm and the unconquerable waves, it still seemed—asway on the water—like a faint prospect of ultimate salvation.

## CHAPTER XLIII

## THE PHŒNICIAN STEERSMAN

ABOARD the Phœnician trireme Xerxes thought of a thousand and one things. He was pale, his eyes were dull and hollowed, and he allowed the barber to neglect his blue-black beard. During the past month of wretchedness he had scarce changed the garments beneath his armour. While he lay downcast, as though disembodied, behind a curtain, the monotonous rowing chant of the Phœnician oarsmen echoing in his ears like an inconsolable threnody, he thought of Mardonius, who had remained behind with the picked warriors. He had to exert himself vividly to recall that last

[223]

review in order to reanimate his daunted courage.
The impossible seemed to have come to pass, and
might come to pass again. He thought of Mardonius, who had remained behind. He thought of
Uncle Artabanus, the old woman, who always had
opposed the war. Was this the end? It could not
be. Mardonius would conquer. And yet—to have
to return thus to Susa!

He would hold a triumphal procession, after all.
It made a better impression. He had sent but few
letters to his uncle and to the women. He had found
it impossible to frame them, impossible to think up
the fine phrases, ending with the finest phrase of all:
the God of the Persians will continue to aid us. The
sacred chariot stolen! The Nisæan steeds stolen!

And, blowing without a break, this everlasting
wind in the waters of the Ægean Sea, surely always
inimical to the Persians! How it was blowing
again! Grey clouds shadowed the sky, and the ship
lurched to the right and to the left. The oarsmen
groaned as they sang and the rudder groaned as it
cleaved the waves. The sails were reefed. The trireme crashed as though its every side-plank had been
stove in.

Xerxes leaped violently from his couch. With
one jolt he tore down the curtains. He saw the
storm. The inexorable autumnal gale was tearing
with greedy claws at the rigging. On deck a number of officers, some of Xerxes' nephews among
them, were clinging to each other. The steersman
tore at his rudder again and again in a mute rage.

"Steersman," cried Xerxes, "are we in danger?"

"Yes, Basileus!"

"Yet there is every hope that we'll be saved, is
there not?" Xerxes angrily queried.

[224]

"Not the slightest, Despot, unless this overladen ship be lightened."

"Overladen? I left nearly all my baggage behind."

"Overladen with men, Basileus."

The autumn tempest raged in its fury like the god of vengeance, buffeting the trireme, which flung from left to right in the seas, unable to advance.

"Then," cried Xerxes, "I command that the Phœnician oarsmen fling themselves overboard!"

"Who is to row in that case, Lord? Your Persians cannot row like the Phœnicians. If the Phœnician oarsmen fling themselves into the sea we shall surely sink."

"Persians," Xerxes then cried, "the moment has come to prove your love for your king! My life is in your hands."

The thickly crowded Persians, clinging to each other, hesitate. Those higher in rank push forward their inferiors. They fling themselves at Xerxes' feet as though in adoration. Then they rise and leap into the sea. After the commoners have leaped the nobles do so. To the left and to the right they leap from the swaying ship. The huge breakers fling many of the victims back on deck. The feet of those surrounding the king thrust them back into the water. The rowing chant of the oarsmen continues sounding like a dirge. The lightened trireme rears on the raging waves.

The following morning the storm has died down. The coast is grey beneath the still lashing wind. It is the Æolian coast, that is to say, Asia. It means salvation for the precious royal life.

Xerxes goes ashore. He bestows on the steersman

a golden wreath, a high distinction, because he has saved the king's life.

Then he has his head cut off, because that same steersman is responsible for the death of a hundred Persians. In this there is no cruelty. The royal decree represents a logical deduction.

## CHAPTER XLIV

## RETURN TO SUSA

AFTER a short stay in Sardis, Xerxes returned to Susa. He did not return as Æschylus, the poet-warrior of Salamis about whom the Muses fluttered, had seen him on the night of the naval combat, on the violet-tinted rocks facing the amethystine sea. He did not return to Susa with the impressive symbolism of torn garments and empty quiver. Nor did he return alone, like the protagonist of the tragedy. He returned amid his many nephews, brothers-in-law and brothers, all of whom had not fallen. He did not return with the Immortals, who had stayed with Mardonius, yet

Hydarnes rode beside him, and a numerous army of
Medes and Persians followed the sonorous hoof-
beats of the King of Kings and of his ever-splendid
staff. Xerxes sat his horse with arrogance, and
lashed his arrogance to an even higher pitch. The
multitude in the streets watched him pass by in
silence. He had been tactful enough, incidentally, to
rid his entry of any semblance of vainglorious
triumph.

The road from the great city gate to the nearest
gate of the palace—a city in itself—was short. The
army at once dispersed to its barracks and into winter
quarters. A cold wind was blowing, bringing with
it stray snowflakes from the Hyrcanian Sea.

In the palace Xerxes at once secluded himself. He
was taciturn and arrogant to his uncle Artabanus
because the latter had been right when he had advised
against the war with Greece. He received his mother
Atossa with reverence, as court etiquette demanded
so venerable a woman should be received. But then
he declared he was weary. Since his garments were
not rent, as Æschylus has pictured them in his
tragedy, it was needless for Atossa to have new robes
made ready for him, as Æschylus had further
imagined. Xerxes did, however, grant a momentary
interview to his wife, Amestris, who brought him a
mantle.

"Lord and husband," said Amestris, pointing to
the four slave-girls who carried over their arms a
multi-coloured mantle completely covered with the
gloss of gold. "Behold! I have woven this mantle
for you with my own hands, in the solitude of the
women's apartments."

(Amestris had always formed part of the circle

of Darius' royal widows and the other princesses. There had been talk enough and to spare.)

"In the solitude of the women's apartments," repeated Amestris, with tearful emphasis. "Lord and husband, may I hope that my work will please you, and that this mantle will hang from your royal shoulders?"

"Very nice, very nice. I am obliged to you, Amestris," said Xerxes nervously, and motioned away the slave-girls who were approaching him with the widespread mantle. The girls retreated and spread out the mantle over a settee.

Amestris was angry, and went away offended. Xerxes remained alone. The palace was silent. It was all so large, so extended, so far from Greece and from Salamis that it hardly seemed as though anything had happened. Xerxes, pacing up and down in the room, flinging himself on a couch, thought: What really *has* happened?

Nothing seemed to have happened. Everything seemed like a dream: Mount Athos cut in half; the Hellespont bridged; the passage of the host that swelled from day to day until it formed a stream of millions; Thermopylæ and the diadem the mad King of Sparta had torn from his brow; the taking of Athens; and the terrible, inconceivable, unthinkable sea-fight at Salamis.

Had all this taken place? It seemed like a dream. Now he had returned and all was as before. The Persian empire, enormous, immeasurable, just as everything about him was immeasurable, Susa, his capital city, nothing was changed.

Yet it was. Three of his brothers had died: Hyperanthes, Abrocomes and Ariabignes. Blood relatives in his entourage often died, although as a

[229]

rule at a more advanced age than these two brave generals and an admiral of the fleet. A dream? No, it was no dream. It was the truth. Mardonius was still in Thessaly, and with him were the Immortals.

Then Xerxes, comfortably stretched out on his pillows, grew despondent. It was no dream. It was the bitter truth. The god of Persia had not aided him. It was most annoying—the theft of the sacred chariot and of the Nisæan steeds. And yet—Zeus would not have been so angered with him for such a cause.

To think that Persia—he admitted it fleetingly to himself—had not secured all for which she had striven! That day at Salamis—incredible! Yet his own eyes had witnessed it. Incredible, incredible! After all, he had not attempted aught impossible for a King of Kings! Only world empire. What objection was there to Persia's ruling the world, Asia and Europe? There was no objection. Persia was the most splendidly organized empire that had ever existed. The ancient Egyptian civilization could not compare with Persia's inner cohesion. Nor could the civilizations of Assyria and Babylon. Omnipotence on earth had been decreed for Persia, for him, Xerxes. Cyrus and his never-to-be-forgotten father Darius had smoothed the way for him. It had been his place to take the matter in hand. He had mishandled it. It had been a rank failure.

Xerxes rose. His room was cold. The open windows gave on a roofless colonnade. The view of the frayed and crumpled gardens was depressing. The long trunks of the palm-trees were bent, and stray snowflakes made an eerie impression in this oriental southland, in this broad royal chamber which could be shut off from the outside only by curtains. Xerxes shuddered.

Then his aimless, almost witlessly wandering glance happened to light on the mantle, Amestris' gift. It lay spread over the settee. It was very handsome, imperial scarlet in colour, with a broad hem of blackish blue. The golden gloss permeated the entire fabric. It was a magnificent mantle, thought Xerxes. He took it up and with a single cast flung it about him.

It was a long Median mantle, trailing a little, with wide sleeves, one of those mantles worn by women as well as by men on festive occasions. Xerxes, after he had regarded himself in the polished golden mirror set in the wall, decided that the mantle was becoming to him. He was still young and, as he looked at himself in the mirror, he began to feel decidedly cocky. In the days since Salamis, during the retreat, he had hardly allowed himself time to loosen his girdle. Now he felt like a stag in rutting-time.

Mardonius, over yonder in Greece, would bring the war to a satisfactory conclusion. Here, Xerxes felt himself obsessed by pelvic ardours. Yet who was to satisfy his urge? The concubines? No. Amestris? No. It would look as though he wished to express special thanks for the mantle. He wanted something adorable, something young, something tender. He did not know who or what.

The King of Kings felt very unhappy in his magnificent mantle, though he would not admit it to himself. He had an attack of melancholia. It often followed immediately upon an attack of arrogance or self-satisfied conceit. He could no longer endure his loneliness.   He struck the great gong which hung like a sun between two bronze columns.

"Send in the boys!" ordered Xerxes.

The eunuch Hermotimus led in the three little lads.   Xerxes was very fond of them.   He caressed them.   They were his three favourite sons.   He made them gifts of jewels, gave them sweetmeats to eat, and admired them.   They appealed to him as kittens might.   And that was as it should be.   They told him about their return with Artemisia, who had brought them to Ephesus.   Thence Hermotimus had taken them to Susa.

"O look!" suddenly said the oldest of the three boys.   "There goes Artaynte!"

"Who is Artaynte?" asked Xerxes, looking out.

"She is the daughter of Uncle Masistes," said the second boy.

"And of Aunt Artaxixa," the third added, in a high, piping treble.

Xerxes, gazing out the window, saw a young princess, the daughter of his brother Masistes, walking in the garden.   She was very lovely, very young. She laughed bewitchingly amid her women, as all of them, to protect themselves against the wind and the driving snowflakes, wrapped their colourful mantles closer around them.   They were followed by eunuchs.

"Artaynte?" Xerxes said to the eunuch Hermotimus, who was waiting in the portico until the king would have finished with his sons.

"Yes, Basileus.   She must be returning to the women's apartments after having welcomed her father."

Xerxes hardly knew her; he no longer recognized her.   He found this little niece delightfully young,

[232]

beautiful and virginal. He whispered two words to Hermotimus.

"Yes, Basileus," answered the eunuch, and bowed to earth before him.

"Take the boys away!" commanded Xerxes.

## CHAPTER XLV

## AMESTRIS' MANTLE

TWO weeks later Artaynte, the beautiful girl, stood before Xerxes, who was seated. She was very proud of the love the king, her uncle, bore her.

"Artaynte!" said Xerxes. "Tell me what you want. I will give you a gift of price."

Artaynte already had long known what she wanted.

"Will you grant me what I ask, my prince and uncle?" Artaynte asked, smiling in the full consciousness of her charms.

"I swear by Persia's supreme god that I will," said Xerxes.

This was the irresponsible oath that Persian kings swore, now and again, and from which they found it hard to free themselves when difficulties resulted.

Artaynte, as her little hands still lay clasped in Xerxes' own, was thinking—as a true Persian princess, brought up amid the constant intrigues of the harem, would think—of her future. Around her were so many youthful nieces that this future worried her, off and on, as it worried her mother Artaxixa, pre-eminent in the preparation of preserves.

"Then, Prince and King," said Artaynte, with ingratiating charm, "I wish to become the wife of your son Darius. In that case I will be your daughter-in-law, Xerxes, and the heiress apparent of Persia."

Xerxes frowned. He was disappointed because in this moment of reward, following upon weeks of unconstrained surrender, Artaynte's first thought was to become his son's wife.

"Darius is still very young," remarked Xerxes, "and he is really supposed to marry some one or another of your little nieces, Artaynte."

"I am well aware of that," said Artaynte, "but I want to be Darius' first wife. Later on I will be queen."

"It is impossible, Artaynte."

"It is so possible," Artaynte obstinately insisted. "I want to be Darius' first wife."

"Perhaps he can take you as a second wife."

"No, no," Artaynte obstinately insisted. "I want to be a queen."

"You can marry Artaxerxes, Artaynte."

[235]

Xerxes was trying to appease her.

"I will not," Artaynte obstinately insisted. "Artaxerxes is still a child. Darius is only a few years younger than I am. I want to marry my cousin Darius and be Queen of Persia. Uncle and Prince, you swore you would grant what I asked."

"Well, perhaps you are not asking too much," Xerxes was obliged to admit. "It's settled, Artaynte. We will see to it that you become Darius' first wife."

"And that later I will become Queen of Persia?"

"Yes, later, later, Artaynte."

"Then I have another wish," said Artaynte, who now first advanced the wish that lay nearest her heart.

"What else, Artaynte?" Xerxes asked, somewhat alarmed. Tenderly and ingratiatingly Artaynte freed her little hands from Xerxes' clasp. She retreated as though she were preparing to dance. But she did not dance. Retreating, she reached the settee on which lay outspread the magnificent mantle, the mantle Amestris had woven for Xerxes.

Then Artaynte, as she stretched out her hands to take the mantle, said:

"I would like to own this mantle."

Xerxes was violently alarmed.

Artaynte had already wrapped herself in the Median mantle.

The imperial scarlet with the blue-black hem saturated with a golden gloss set her off as though she already were Persia's queen.

"That is impossible, Artaynte," said Xerxes angrily.

"It is," insisted Artaynte obstinately, wrapping herself more closely in the mantle. She looked at

[236]

herself in the shining inset wall-mirror, as Xerxes himself had done. She turned this way and that.

"It really is impossible, Artaynte!" said Xerxes, red with rage. "Amestris wove the mantle for me during the war. I cannot let you have the mantle."

"I want this mantle!" insisted Artaynte obstinately, watching her reflection as she spoke. "I saw Aunt Amestris weaving it. I know all about it. It is not a very good piece of work. It has defects. Look, there, on the hem! But I want to have it, notwithstanding. I shall not return the mantle, Uncle Xerxes. I shall keep the mantle. It now belongs to me."

"Really, Artaynte?"

"You swore to grant me whatever I might ask."

"Yes, but you asked . . ."

"I ask for very little. I only ask to be Darius' first wife, and later on Queen of Persia. And all I ask besides is this mantle. It is not even very well woven."

Xerxes clenched his fists in despair, tried to control himself, attempted to reason with her.

"Artaynte," he said in kind and gentle tones, yet at the same time haughtily and regally, as a princely lover should who must confront his new, young favourite. "Artaynte, it is impossible. It really is, my dear child. It is out of the question. Ask something else of me."

"I will not."

"Ask me for some cities!"

"I want no cities," said Artaynte, "I want the mantle."

"Ask me for gold, as much gold as you wish!"

"But I want no gold. I have gold and to spare,

[237]

and when I am Queen of Persia I shall have all the gold in the world."

"Then ask me for an army, Artaynte! An army is the greatest gift a Persian king can give, an army you yourself can command."

"I do not want to command an army," said Artaynte. "I want to have this mantle. You promised me the mantle, Uncle Xerxes. You must give it to me. Otherwise you will be breaking your royal word, and I shall tell father about it. I shall tell Masistes that Xerxes broke his royal word."

She suddenly wrapped the mantle around her and stood proudly erect, like a little fury. She dared him. The Persian princesses were the slaves of their fathers, brothers, uncles and nephews. But when they felt so inclined they turned them into slaves.

"Then at least take care that Amestris does not see you wearing it!" said Xerxes, as Artaynte laughed and crept away in the garment, which hung heavily and royally about her.

For the first few days she wore the mantle only in front of her own mirror, wherein she admired herself in various poses a future Queen of Persia might be expected to strike. Then she grew bolder, since the mantle was so becoming. She ventured out beyond the porticoes clad in it. Her mother Artaxixa warned her. The royal widows Phaidyme and Parmys saw her parading boastfully about in it through the palm-grove in the gardens.

Then gossipy whispers began to circulate from one to the other of the many princesses, concubines and slaves in the women's apartments. Artaynte was the favourite wife of the Basileus and was wearing the mantle which Amestris had woven for Xerxes during the war. Not all of them would believe it. The women came and secretly peered at her from behind the columns.

At last Amestris, too, saw her. Amestris raged. She tore herself with her nails in her rage and beat her women with the lash. The women's courtyard was agog with an excitement that almost caused the mourning for brothers, brothers-in law, husbands and nephews to be forgotten, that thrust regrets for the fatal war into the background. The war had run its course in the far distance, in the middle of Europe. But the mantle was on the spot, in Asia, in Susa, and the rise to power of the new favourite wife, Artaynte, was more exciting than the war in Europe, the Ionians and Athens. All the women were whispering about the mantle as they all saw Amestris rage and tear her cheeks with her finger-nails.

There was great curiosity as to what Amestris would do. It seemed as though she would do nothing—until Xerxes' birthday came. On that day a great festival was held in city and in palace. It was the *tykta,* as the Persians say, the "Perfected Festival." For days in advance the cooks were busy in the kitchens preparing enormous quantities of meat and sweet fruit-cakes. The bakers baked thousands of small loaves in symbolic forms. And the confectioners used the same forms in the preparation of their sweet-meats. Sweet palm-wines were spiced and mixed with bayberry honey.

On that day, after sacrifices have been made to the gods, amid dances, games and song, the blessing of the royal head takes place. Priests anoint the king's forehead and temples. The fragrant oils drip down upon his blue-black beard. The heavy oils spread their fragrance throughout the palace.

For that one day Xerxes had borrowed the mantle from Artaynte. He sat wrapped in the mantle while his priests anointed him.

Then he ate alone, on a raised seat. He was served by his nearest blood relatives. On the cloth of gold tablecloth, with gold fringes that hung over the steps, all the vessels from which he ate and drank were one glow of gold. The entire court watched the king, and the populace glimpsed him from afar. It crowded behind the marble bars in order to snatch a glimmer of the glitter and the sanctity of the royal meal.

At first the king ate and drank with solemnity. His every movement in connection therewith was a ceremonial which Xerxes carried out with grace and regal self-consciousness. Then came the moment when he was to present gifts to his family, the whole court and the people, and grant whatever request anyone might make of him.

It was not safe for a petitioner to show himself too grasping. Yet the law of the royal house forbade the king to deny any request. Since Atossa, because of her extreme age, was not present at the celebration, the queen was the first to advance. The king rose with perfected grace, conscious that all eyes were resting on him, and asked Amestris what she demanded.

"Great Despot!" said Amestris. "Your slave begs that you will give her the mantle."

Xerxes was frightened. Yet there was no refusing her. Court officials divested Xerxes of the mantle and approached Amestris with it.

Then, as Amestris drew the heavy cloak around her she added:

"And Artaynte."

Now Xerxes paled. At one and the same time he inwardly raged and trembled.

No matter what might happen to the queen because of her lack of modesty, he could refuse her nothing. In the midst of the other princesses Artaynte uttered a shriek of horror. But refusal was out of the question. She was led over to Amestris, who departed, giving orders that Artaynte was to be led after her.

It was outrageous—but Amestris had avenged herself. The people, standing in the far distance, did not understand, but regarded all the glittering pomp with wide-open mouths. Amid the brothers-in-law, brothers and nephews, amid all the princesses and women, amid all the thousands of courtiers, rose a babel of voices. Those concerned forgot to beg for gifts and favours.

"What does Amestris wish to do to my daughter, Prince and Lord?" asked Masistes, Artaynte's father.

Xerxes, minus his mantle, yet still full of dignity, murmured something. It was indistinguishable. General confusion ensued. The colonnaded porticoes resounded with the clatter of raging lashes. A little baker, who was carrying pastries and sweetmeats on a tray of woven reeds, was overturned and trampled.

It was something unheard of, said the royal widows and Artozostra, Mardonius' wife. The porticoes were thronged with women and full of the soft murmur of voices. There were passionate explanations, and great was the curiosity as to what Amestris would do to Artaynte. It was generally disapproved that the queen should spoil a holiday like the Perfected Festival with such an uproar. And it was an out-and-out monstrous thing to do it at

[241]

the very moment when so many delicious tarts and confections were ready to be eaten.

In the meantime Artaynte, following Amestris surrounded by a swarm of eunuchs and women, had reached the women's apartments. Amestris, who until now had managed to hold her silent rage in check, turned furiously around and clenched her fists. Cruel and terror-inspiring, she confronted Artaynte, who had dropped to her knees with an imploring gesture.

"Mercy! Mercy!" cried Artaynte, stretching out her hands. "Queen! Royal Aunt! Have mercy!"

"Now you are in my power!" shrieked Amestris while, as though on a rising tide of sensuousness, the froth of sheer cruelty hissed between her teeth. "Now you are in my power. Eunuchs: Call up the torturers! She is mine. This strumpet! She is mine! The king has given her to me! I'll have her breasts cut off and flung to the dogs!"

"Mercy! Mercy!" cried Artaynte, in a voice trembling with despair, writhing on the floor at Amestris' feet.

"I'll have her nose chopped off!"

"Mercy!"

"I'll have her ears sheared, her tongue torn out!"

"Mercy!"

"I'll have her lips cut away!"

Artaynte no longer pleaded for mercy. She screamed, screamed like mad, while her eyes stood out of her head. In terror she already suffered those horrors which sometimes, as a result of hatred and jealousy, occurred in the Persian seraglio, the horrors which, as she had seen with her own eyes, were sometimes inflicted on concubines or slaves, but which hitherto no Persian princess had experienced. It is true that the lash reigned at all times, yet when it proved itself too weak to punish or avenge, then the executioner came with his axe, his pincers and his tongs. There was a rustling that betrayed growing horror among the thickly crowding women who, together with the eunuchs, were jammed between columns and doors, especially when the executioner appeared with his assistants. All were in holiday dress, because it was the Perfected Festival, the king's birthday and the day of his consecration.

At the same moment, in the door which led to the apartments of the royal widows, appeared Atossa. She was very old. Her violet veils hung as thickly and wearily as spiderwebs about her angular limbs, about her grey hair and her wrinkled features. In her skinny, trembling hand hung the whip she always carried, yet could raise only with an effort, because her gouty muscles refused to function. She was impressive as she appeared with her narrowed eyes amid the other royal widows, Artystone, Parmys and Phaidyme, who had called her. She enjoyed the highest consideration, and the women trembled in her presence more than in that of the king himself.

"What's going on here?" she asked in a cool voice.

Amestris stood proudly erect, looking like a fury.

"Allhighest Mother!" she cried. "The Basileus has given me this wanton, and I can do with her what I will. This strumpet, who swaggered about in the mantle I wove for my husband! I'll have her lips cut away, her tongue torn out and her ears and nose chopped off. I'll have her breasts cut off and cast to the dogs!"

[243]

"Allhighest Grandmother!" cried Artaynte, and crawled along the ground to Atossa. "Mercy! Mercy!"

Meanwhile Artaxixa, her mother, with Artozostra, Mardonius' wife, had entered, violently excited. They had begged Xerxes to show mercy to Artaynte. Xerxes had said he could do nothing about it, and he must now distribute marks of favour and gifts to his officers and palace officials.

Then, like a snake, a whip circled through the air. Its lashes rained down on Artaynte's bare back. The girl shrieked with pain. A little blood ran purple down her neck. "Away!" cried Atossa furiously. "Don't you hear? Into your room, strumpet!"

Again the old woman raised the whip. But it missed its mark. Slave-girls competed as to which should seize it. Crawling on all fours, they offered her the whip, writhing at her feet with their hands held high.

Yet what the old woman, the daughter of Cyrus, who was the supreme ruler in the harem and about whom legend already had spun a veil of terrifying awe, what the old woman had done was tantamount to pardon. Artaxixa pulled her daughter to her feet, her slave-girls ran up, and a third stroke of the whip pointed out the way to the princess, guilty—but pardoned. "Into your room!"

Artaynte fled out of the ring of women. Amestris screamed, like a bloodthirsty beast cheated of its prey.

"The Basileus gave her to me!" she shrieked furiously, into Atossa's very face.

The whip rose. The whip circled through the air like a snake. The whip threatened Amestris, the Queen of Persia, and between the narrowed lids of

[244]

the Allhighest Mother flashed rage, flashed inviolable authority.

Amestris cried her humiliation to the very columns. Her hands clenched in convulsive rage. She kept on screaming, and betrayed her hysterical impotence by a stifled sobbing.

"The queen to *her* room!" Atossa hissed between her old wrinkled lips, in overwhelming agitation. "I rule here, I, I!"

All trembled. Amestris obeyed. Her slave-women ringed her about and supported her, while she beat about her with her fists and writhed like some wild beast that has been subdued. The eunuchs closed around her, respectfully drawing back the curtains from the doors.

Atossa slowly glanced around through those eyes ever blinking because of age and illness in her distorted face. All were silent. No one spoke. Among all those motionless women, princesses, concubines and slaves, not a voice was raised. Then Atossa slowly turned her back on them. She went off with Darius' other royal widows, Artystone, Parmys, Phaidyme. About Artaxixa and Artozostra there at once sounded the rustle of a hundred female voices, no longer to be suppressed.

"Now she has her deserts," said Artaynte's mother, alluding to her daughter.

There were lively discussions. From the porticoes streamed in the sweet fragrance of the cakes, and of all the symbolic sweetmeats that had been baked for the Perfected Festival.

"But that's no reason why we should not enjoy these delicious things," added Artaxixa.

All agreed with her. The train of slave-girls approached, carrying pastries and confections on

[245]

reed platters. They moved almost solemnly, with religious unction, carrying on their heads or in arms outstretched in hieratic postures all sorts of delightfully smelling tidbits.

"We'll send Amestris some of them," said Artaxixa.

"And Artaynte," added Artozostra, full of pity.

"And the royal widows," rose a murmur round about. Artaxixa and Artozostra made a selection among the dainties, and the slave-girls with their loaded platters unctuously betook themselves to the royal widows, to Amestris, and to the deplorable Artaynte.

That evening the Perfected Festival ran its course as though nothing untoward had occurred.

## CHAPTER XLVI

## THE THOUGHTS OF MARDONIUS

WINTER was over. The early southern spring passed in a fragrance of almond-bloom over Hellas, and over Thessaly, where Mardonius and his army had gone into winter quarters amid the princes of that land, who were well-inclined toward him. The Athenians, who had re-entered their burned city—only in part rebuilt because of the uncertainty of the immediate future—and the Peloponnesians, who had completed their wall across the Isthmus of Corinth, thought the moment had arrived to send their combined fleet of one hundred and ten ships to Ægina.

Leutychides, son of Menares, was strategus and monarch of the Peloponnesian, Xantippus, son of Ariphron, of the Athenian ships.

For Themistocles was learning Persian. Themistocles was learning Persian after establishing the triple harbour of Piræus at Athens, because the bay of Phaleron was too small for a rising naval power like Athens'. Themistocles, after he had surrounded Athens with walls—as an envoy in Sparta he had dragged along negotiations until the walls girding Athens were an accomplished fact—Themistocles was learning Persian. For what reason he himself might not have been able to say, offhand. It is possible that he sensed that Athens might not, in the long run, love a man who became too powerful in the state, who did and had done too much, and who had raised the state too greatly above the other Hellenic states in the general esteem. It is possible that Themistocles was learning Persian because of this. It may be that he foresaw what later was to come to pass: Sparta's furious complaints that he had made common cause with the Persian king, his subsequent banishment and flight.

His flight to Persia for the moment still lay in the distant future, yet Themistocles, as though he anticipated it, was learning Persian.

In the meantime Mardonius was working out the plans for his great offensive. He went over them with his friends, the Thessalian princes, and even went further. He sent Mys, a Greek, not a Persian, to all the Hellenic oracles. Yet it seemed as though Mardonius, after his splendid gesture, after kneeling before Xerxes and assuring him that he would force the Greeks under the Persian yoke or die in the attempt, had grown gloomy and suspicious. That winter of tense expectancy in Thessaly seemed like banishment. Mys returned with the varying answers of the various oracles, and these were not calculated to cheer him.

Before he decided upon his great, decisive offensive Mardonius suddenly seized upon the idea of offering peace to the Greeks.

What real sense was there in this war? He had urged it out of revenge for his defeat ten years before. But then he was still an enthusiastic young captain, a radiant prince, who saw great goals gleaming before him, and who in Susa, surrounded by the effeminacy and intrigues of the seraglio, had been bored. What real sense was there in this war? To take vengeance for the irruptions of the Greeks into Asia Minor? Mardonius hardly remembered them. He seemed to have aged more than ten years, he, Xerxes' brother-in-law, during these lazily dragging months which had followed on the defeat of Salamis and the king's flight. Like Xerxes, he no longer slept. He no longer was sure of what he wanted. He was almost disinclined to continue the war. He longed for Persia, for Susa, for his wife, Artozostra, for his young children. He felt as though some hidden power were acting against him, a fate lurking in this inimical air, for all that in these days it might be saturated with the fragrance of almond-blossoms.

It seemed as though the gods of Hellas were floating somewhere back of those slowly drifting springtide clouds in the blue ether, as though they would be stronger than Persia's gods, no matter what Xerxes might claim.

Mardonius felt weary and homesick. To Athens he sent a distinguished envoy, Alexander, son of

Amyntas, Prince of Macedon, very friendly to Persia, of Persian blood, an out-and-out Persian in soul, and yet on a friendly footing with the Athenians, whom he had done many favours of old. Mardonius sent Alexander to Athens in order to induce that sturdy young naval power not to reject the hand Persia offered. Then, thought Mardonius, he would soon get the better of the allies on land.

It was a mirage, born of his enervation. It was a moment of weakness for which Mardonius could hardly account to himself.

Mardonius offered peace.

## CHAPTER XLVII

## THE REJECTED PEACE OFFER

ALEXANDER said to the Athenians assembled:
"Athenians! Hark to the tidings Mardonius sends you by my mouth. I have had
word from the king. He says: 'I forgive the Athenians for their offences.'"

This beginning of Alexander's speech was subtle
and impenetrable. The "I" form referred first of all
to Alexander, then to Mardonius and finally to
Xerxes. Those who stood some distance away did
not, at first, understand this threefold form of the
first personal pronoun at all. For a moment it

[251]

looked as though Alexander were forgiving the Athenians for their offences.

What offences had they committed? These first words of Alexander won him no favour with his listeners. Yet Alexander, well aware of his skill as an orator, and of the old obligations under which Athens lay to Macedon, continued to report the message Xerxes had sent Mardonius:

"Therefore do as I command, Mardonius, and give their land back to the Athenians!"

The Athenians standing farthest removed were only now beginning to grasp his meaning, though an Athenian was anything but slow-witted. Yet the form of address chosen by Alexander was too circumlocutious.

"Tell them that they are to select some other territory near Attica, whichever they wish!"

Distant King Xerxes, in far-away Susa, was disposing of things quite high-handedly, thought the Athenians.

"They are to live according to their own laws!"

They never would do aught else.

"That I, if they wish to enter into an alliance with me, the King of Kings, will command that their burned temples be rebuilt."

That was it! A murmur was audible in the assembly, a noise, a rustling. An alliance with Xerxes? Never!

"I shall put these orders into execution," continued Alexander, as though now he were Mardonius, "if you place no hindrances in my way. Now I speak to you in my own name."

"He is speaking in Mardonius' name," said the Athenians standing farthest away.

"He is saying what Mardonius told him."

Alexander went on.

"What folly it is to declare war on the King of Kings!"

"He declared war on us!" cried the Athenians noisily.

"It is his fault, it is Xerxes' fault."

"You will never defeat him, and you will not always be able to withstand him. His great deeds are known to you as well as the number of his armies. And you have also heard of *my* host."

"What is he saying?" asked the more distant. "Whose host?"

"That of Mardonius," declared the Athenians nearer by.

"Even though you should defeat my army which, if you are wise, you can hardly imagine, still mightier hosts will come to avenge me. Do you think yourselves on a par with Persia? Do you wish to lose your homeland and your lives? If not, become reconciled to the Great King!"

"No!" cried the Athenians standing farther away, who had understood.

"See to it that you accept his favour!"

"What favour? No!"

"More honourable conditions never will be offered you, Athenians."

There was a violent commotion. Alexander, however, continued:

"Behold, Athenians! That is what Mardonius bade me say to you."

"Is he at last speaking for himself?" some dissatisfied voices called out.

"So far as I am concerned, I shall now prove how well inclined I am toward you."

"He is a Persian. He is a Barbarian . . ."

"My advice is: Do not reject Mardonius' offer. You will not be able to withstand Xerxes to the end."

"He fled from us after Salamis."

"If I knew you were strong enough to withstand him to the end I would not come to you with this proposal. The king's power is limitless, super-human. If you do not conclude an alliance with Persia on such favourable terms . . ."

The noise was deafening. Alexander's words were submerged in the sea of furious sound.

"So I fear for you, for you in particular. Among all the allies you are most exposed to Xerxes' vengeance. You will once again be the first war victims. What the Great King offers you is priceless. Among all the Hellenes you are the only ones whose friendship he desires."

No sooner had Alexander concluded his speech to the accompaniment of a tremendous uproar, than the Lacedæmonian envoys, who had attended the gathering, rose as a man, with great dignity. Their spokesman said:

"Athenians! Sparta sends us to beg that you accept no proposals detrimental to Hellas. You should not give ear to Xerxes' offer. An alliance with Persia would be shameful. You wanted the war, against Sparta's will."

There was a tumult.

Sparta wanted the war voices cried. The Athenians called for silence.

The Spartan spokesman went on:

"At first the war was only your affair."

There was noisy denial.

"Now the war is the affair of us all."

There were joyous shouts, like those of school-boys dismissed from school.

"Would you, after having caused this misfortune . . ."

There were violent demonstrations of sympathy among the people. Hissing, silence was insisted upon.

". . . would you now wish to see Hellas bow beneath the Persian yoke? Do you, Athenians, who always have defended the freedom of peoples, wish to see that?"

There was tremendous jubilation, one great cry from a thousand mouths against tyranny, against conquest, against him who sought world empire for himself alone.

The Spartan had won. When silence had once more fallen he went on in low tones:

"Athenians! Whatever you suffer, we suffer with you. Your houses are heaps of ruins. You have not harvested for two years. With entire understanding of your sufferings, we offer to feed your old folk, your women and children. Do not—we implore you—let yourselves be deluded by Alexander's flattering speeches! He is a tyrant and a tyrant's slave. Be wise! Do not trust a Barbarian! For he is never to be trusted."

Whereupon the Athenians answered Alexander by the mouth of their spokesman:

"It is vain, Alexander, son of Amyntas, for you to puff up the might of the Medes with braggart speeches. We know as well as you do that their host is greater than our own. But aglow with holy zeal we will defend our liberties to the last drop of blood. Do not try to persuade us to form an alliance with Xerxes. We never will do so.

[255]

"Take back Athens' answer to Mardonius, Alexander. So long as the sun rises in the east and sets in the west, we will never bind ourselves to the Barbarians, but confiding in the protection of our gods and heroes, whose temples and images Xerxes destroyed, we will march to meet the tyrant and drive him from our land."

Breathlessly the Athenians had listened. Then a glad, reverential murmur rose from their ranks.

The spokesman went on, and now he spoke threateningly:

"As for you, Alexander, never again deliver such a message to the Athenians! Never again expect us to commit an infamy under the pretext of doing our country a service! For though we are united by the laws of hospitality and friendship, those laws would go by the board."

Alexander turned pale. The Athenian then answered the Spartans:

"The Lacedæmonians' fear that we might treat with the Barbarians is unfounded. Such negotiations would be shameful. No! There is on earth no gold, no land, fair though it might be, that would tempt us to become the allies of the Medes in order to enslave Hellas. We Hellenes are united by the ties of blood and speech. We all pray to the same gods, we all speak the same tongue.

"Spartans! We thank you for your offer to feed our women and children. Yet we will be able to feed them ourselves. And now, since matters stand thus, lead your army to battle. For as soon as the Barbarian learns that we have declined his offer he will think of invading Attica. Let us anticipate him in Bœotia."

There was a violent commotion, cries, cheers, pushing and jostling. Alexander, pale and furious, stood in the square before the Council Hall. A herald approached him and said:

"Alexander, son of Amyntas, I am commanded to inform you that you are to leave Athens before sunset, on pain of death!"

From the tumultuous crowd came the sound of hisses, jeers and abuse. A few stones hurtled through the air.

## CHAPTER LXVIII

## TORCHLIGHT ON THE ACROPOLIS

MARDONIUS, conscious that it was the decree of fate, left Thessaly with the Thessalian princes and his whole army. After some rapid marches the Persians flooded Bœotia and occupied friendly Thebes. Had not Leonidas always mistrusted his Theban hostages?

The Thebans tried to induce Mardonius not to hurry on so rapidly.

"Farther on you will find no suitable place to encamp. Take our advice and send money into the Greek cities! They will fall out among each other and discord will rule. Together with those whose

[258]

favour you gain you will overcome the recalcitrants. If all remain united you will not so easily become master of Hellas."

In the fever which burned in him like some consuming fire, Mardonius paid no attention to the words of the Persophile Thebans.

He swept into Attica like a spring flood. For the second time the Persians took Athens, ten months after its first capture, and Mardonius—though the city was completely deserted, the Athenians once more having taken refuge on their ships before Salamis—triumphantly commanded that the fall of Athens be reported to the king in Asia.

It was done even more swiftly than the splendidly organized Persian postal service could have done it—by torch-signal, as Æschylus, the poet-warrior, in his *Agamemnon* has Clytemnestra informed of the fall of Troy. When a torch is lit on one of the towers of Athens, it is at once visible many stadia away. The watchman on a second tower in the Thriasian plain sees the flame in the night. He now lights his torch. Farther along, the third torch reporting victory gleams out in the darkness. The length of the coast, along the long road the torches flare, and, glow to glow, weld the chain of flaming cressets. And even before night dissolves in grey dawn Xerxes knows, every Persian knows, that Athens has fallen a second time. The stenography of fire, in the summer night, has written her flaming signs, that say Mardonius has taken the city, on the nocturnal air from Athens to Susa.

The Athenians had not found time to oppose the Persians in Bœotia. The Athenian envoys reproached the Lacedæmonians—who were celebrating their Hyacinthia, the spring festival of Hyacinthus, beloved of Apollo—with the delay. They advised the allies that now, at least, they might join them to offer the Persians battle in the Thriasian plain. Alliances exist, but there is always the selfishness of separate states just as, in spite of all friendship, there is always the selfishness of individuals. The wall across the Isthmus of Corinth was nearly completed. At bottom the Peloponnesians had little reason to fear the Persians. Apollo, however, was the supreme god, and the Hyacinthia were the festivals which celebrate the death and rebirth of holy nature. Were the Lacedæmonians to fail in piety because the Persians invaded Attica?

After a ten days' delay, during which the protecting wall was completely finished, the Spartan Ephors replied to the Athenians that five thousand Spartans were on the way to Athens. Each was accompanied by seven helots, as they called their slaves.

The King of Sparta, who should have been the leader of the Lacedæmonian forces, was Pleistarchus, Leonidas' son. But the boy was hardly more than a child, playing at war with other little boys. And when Gorgo, the blonde young wife of the royal paladin who will ever remain the hero of Thermopylæ, leads him to his cousin and guardian Pausanias, son of Cleombrotus, who will be captain of the Lacedæmonians, Pausanias bends down and embraces the little king. The group and the moment are so chastely beautiful that the blue spring sky seems quivering to a Homeric rhythm.

## CHAPTER XLIX

## THE CORPSE-LIGHT

MARDONIUS heard that the Spartans were approaching. No matter how many intrigues he may have initiated with the cities of Argolis, they have borne no fruit. Their swiftest *hunedromos*, or day-runner, had come to report the Spartan advance to him. Mardonius decided not to stay in Athens. He would fight a battle on the broad Thriasian plain or still farther north, beyond the Cithæron, on the plain of Platæa.

Once more Athens went up in flames. Again walls and buildings were razed while demolishing sledges swung. And not they alone—Mardonius did not even spare the temples of the gods. It is ever the Barbarian's fate that in the blindness of a tragic moment he does not spare what the holy cult of humanity had consecrated. Yet if ever he is reproached therewith, he will be able to make the same reproach in turn, and everything and everybody, the world at large, is to blame. For times and men do not change.

Couriers follow one on the other. They reported that a thousand Lacedæmonians were coming to Megara. They reported that the greater part of their army had marched to the Isthmus, to defend the wall.

Then Mardonius, too, ordered that a wall be built along the Æsopus river, and his army lay encamped from Erythræa to Platæa.

In Thebes Attaginus, son of Phrynon, gave a great banquet in honour of Mardonius. Fifty distinguished Persians lay about the table with Mardonius, as well as fifty Thebans. Each couch was shared by a Theban and a Persian. Wine brimmed the cups. There were sumptuous dishes, games, dances, songs.

A Persian asked Thersandrus of Orchomenus, lying with him at table:

"Where do you hail from, comrade?"

"From Orchomenus," answered Thersandrus. "But tell me in turn, comrade, why you are so disturbed?"

For the Persian, who had asked his question only to comply with the courtesies of the occasion, had grown very pale. His eyelids trembled, his hands shook.

The Persian replied:

"Shall I tell you what has caused the emotion I

[262]

am unable to hide under cover of our table-talk? Then listen, Thersandrus of Orchomenus, so that, in days to come, you may guard a memory of me, who drank with you out of the same cup, a memory that may be of use to you."

The Persian grasped Thersandrus' arm and said:

"Do you see all our fellow banqueters lying here?"

"Yes," replied Thersandrus, gazing slowly about him.

"And over yonder between the columns and curtains, do you see the army glittering on the plain?"

"I see it," answered Thersandrus.

"Do you see nothing else?" queried the Persian, shuddering.

"What else is there to see?"

"Don't you see that strange light?"

"It's a cloudy day, the sun is hidden."

"But don't you see the faint bluish light overspreading the sea?"

"No."

"Don't you see the pale, awesome shimmering, as pallid as that spread by approaching dissolution, like a dragging mist?"

"I do not see it. Do you?"

"I see it."

"You are a man with a gift. You have the second sight."

"I see the mist. I see the exhalation. It comes from without. Look! It spreads awesomely like a greyish shimmer above the tints, above the soldiers yonder. And look—here! Here in this room the strange shimmer floats about like the colour of death itself, above Mardonius, and above nearly all the Persians surrounding him."

[263]

The two table-partners looked at each other with pallid faces.

"Now you are disturbed, as I am," said the Persian.

"I am disturbed," rejoined Thersandrus. "You see all this?"

"I see it."

"What does the strange apparition foretell?"

"Death! Of all these Persians, of all these countrymen of mine, only a few will ever see the sun again a few days hence. I myself . . ."

He hesitated. He groped around as though he could feel the cold he could not see about him.

"I do not know my own fate," he said and trembled. "Yet all they . . ." His motion embraced the tables.

"Will they be dead?" asked Thersandrus.

"Many of them."

The Persian wept, hiding his face behind his drinking-cup.

"Why is Mardonius not informed?"

Again the Persian laid his hand on Thersandrus' arm.

"Nay, my host," he said, "what God has decreed cannot be turned aside, and those who will not believe, do not even believe in what is beyond question. Yet look about you."

"I am doing so. I see many Persians who . . ."

"Speak!"

"Who are as pale and disturbed as you are. Have they the second sight?"

"They have," replied the Persian.

And it seemed true. The Persians, pale-faced, looked into each other's eyes and saw the pallid glow,

[264]

the corpse-coloured shimmer, like some ghostly apparition, hover for a brief moment above many heads.

Mardonius saw naught, however, and smiling, cup in hand, offered the libation to the gods while he chatted with his partner Attaginus.

## CHAPTER L

## MASISTIUS' FALL

IVE days later Mardonius had received by the royal courier the king's congratulations on the second taking of Athens. The wax tablets gave him a moment's happiness. Yet he longed for solitude and—in this night, after a day of varied excitement—for a breath of fresh air. He mounted his white charger and Artabazus, son of Pharnakes, accompanied him.

Why this irony of events? Mardonius asked himself, as in silence he rode slowly the length of the camp, while an escort of a few Immortals followed the general with a muffled beat of hoofs. Why this irony? That same day on which Mardonius received Xerxes' congratulations had been one of great remorse and pain for him. The night was now oppressive and starless, almost black, and absolutely mute. The day, this day had been well-nigh too hard for him to bear.

The entrails of the sacrificial beasts, consulted by Hegesistratus, the Elian soothsayer, persistently threatened disaster, and spies had reported that the sacrifices of the Greeks were favourable to them.

The Lacedæmonians had camped directly across the Isthmus, behind the wall. Thereupon, with the Athenians, they had advanced around the wall to the foot of Cithæron. Yet they had not crossed through Cithæron's passes. Protected by the sacred mountain, they seemed to be engaged in long and cautious consultation.

That morning Mardonius had ordered his magnificent cavalry to attack, and Masistius had led out his horsemen. O day of sorrow! How could the night be so strangely calm after all the evil that the day had brought! There was no sound save the dull beat of hoofs in the solitude, above which the black, sultry sky spread its darkness like heavy mourning veils. Masistius, that paladin, on his gold-bridled Nisæan steed, Masistius, as tall and handsome as one of the sacred heroes of Persia whose shades now abide with the gods, Masistius flung himself with his horsemen on the Greeks, and covered them with insult, calling them women who trembled in hiding.

How can Mardonius now inform the king of what occurred? The enemy received reinforcements. Athenians appeared. The Persians lured them through the passes into the plain. The battle began. Masistius—O day of sorrow!—spurred on in advance, too far, too boldly for a general, too impatiently. Suddenly an arrow buried itself in the flank of his splendid steed. Mardonius, from afar, had seen the beast rear, had heard its mad neigh of despair. Then it crashed to earth, falling on its master. The Greeks hurried up, their lances raised, but could not at once make an end of him because of the golden scales of his well-wrought armour. Yet at last they pierced his eye and slew him.

What Mardonius saw from a distance the Persian cavalry saw from near by, though not at once. For they galloped up and then, luring on the foe, immediately fell back again, because among them all not one had seen Masistius fall. Yet at last they saw, and dashed up in order at least to call their leader's corpse their own.

And how they fought for that corpse! When they had conquered it, after an embittered struggle, how they all lamented, how the Persians lamented like women and hired wailers! They shaved off their hair and their beards, they cut off the manes of their horses, and all the hair-tufts of their pack beasts. They displayed the most exceeding grief. All Bœotia re-echoed their lamentations. And the enemy heavens must have trembled at the sound.

Masistius, the hero, was no more. They laid his corpse on a chariot of war and slowly paraded it through the camp. How tall and handsome he had looked as he lay stretched out, for all that his eye had been pierced! How he resembled one of those divine heroes who attend the Persian gods! Surely his soul, too, was now in that azure paradise where Ormuzd sits throned in a glory of light, his staff of winged heroes surrounding him! Yet though glory radiate above, below is the burden of sorrow.

Fate, O terrible fate! What is floating yonder in the air? What threatens in the night? Can it really be Persia's disastrous fate lying in wait? Can the worst really come to pass after Thermopylæ, after tragic Salamis? Can it be that from out those solemn atmospheres something enervating flowed into the strength and hope that dwelt within them, who were the victors, despite all, who had taken Athens for the second time? As Mardonius rode on in silence, Artabazus riding as silently beside him, his escort of Immortals behind them, he felt like crying out to this enigmatic sultry night sky: Can it be possible that I, Mardonius, who wanted and compelled this war, and who have remained when it was best for the king to go, that I am to be defeated by these Dorians and Ionians? Is mighty Persia no longer to be omnipotent, now that Cyrus and Darius are gone?

It cannot be. Mardonius regains his self-command, sits more erect. The quiet, wordless ride is over. Here is Mardonius' tent. He dismounts and enters it with Artabazus. Here may be seen the luxury Xerxes left behind. There stand his gilded throne, his gilded couch, his precious vessels. There, sumptuously spread, are his woven rugs. The lamplight is reflected by all the gold and bronze. The burning wicks wake a glow in the purple walls of the tent. A consultation takes place with the other generals and officers. It is thought best to move the camp more to the west. The wells are clearer; water is abundant there. "What do they call the city near which we will camp?" Mardonius asks.

Through the tent there sounds a name which, like that of Thermopylæ, of Salamis, seems an echo of the voice of Fate:

"Platæa."

[269]

### CHAPTER LI

## THE ORACLE

EIGHT days have passed. At the foot of Cithæron the two armies confront each other on
the plain. On either side there is suspicious
hesitation, on either side there is expectation. It is a
day in late summer. High-piled masses of white
cloud drive along a wind-torn sky. On the bank
of the Æsopus Hegesistratus is sacrificing. Impatiently Mardonius watches the ceremony, as the
soothsayer consults the entrails of the slaughtered
cattle on the altar.

"Are the omens favourable?" Mardonius urgently
demands.

"Not yet," the soothsayer replies.

"The Greek army grows larger day by day," says Mardonius. "All the spies bring in the same report."

"The omens," declares the soothsayer, "are favourable neither to the Persians nor to the Greeks who are with them."

"Nor to the Thebans?"

"Nor to the Thessalians. It is better to wait."

Mardonius cannot control his impatience. Since Masistius' death, especially, his feverish urge at last to take vengeance on the Greeks has grown more pressing. He orders new sacrifices to be made, and another soothsayer, Hippomachus of Leukas, to interpret the sacrificial entrails. Yet the new soothsayer says that the entrails are not sufficiently favourable for the Persians to justify an attack.

Mardonius would like to coerce the gods. Often he is overcome by the same feeling that visited his Persians as they gazed on the apparition at the banquet in Thebes. Just as they had seen the fallow light, and sensed in it the pallid circlet of approaching death, so Mardonius felt, now and again. But he refused to give way to this feeling. This time he meant to conquer, and was sick with impatience to begin. At night he could not sleep on the sumptuous couch Xerxes had left for him.

A few more days go by. The Persians and the Thebans, again and again, ride challengingly down to the river bank and call out insults to the allied Greeks. Why does Fate delay? Why does she cause all that must come to pass to loiter so indolently amid these clouds, these ranges of hills, this river? Why does everything drag along between the tents here by Platæa and the tents yonder at the broad foot of the holy mount, in the wide plain between

[271]

the two camps, separated one from the other, while ever and anon the Persian horsemen, swinging their lances, ride challengingly across the level and the Dorians timidly hesitate.

Already the armies have been facing each other for eleven days. Which will be the first to attack? To which will the gods grant victory, that floats earthward from Zeus' opened hand? No matter how provocative the Persians, the Greeks refuse to attack. The Persians themselves? The entrails of the sacrificial victims remain too consistently unfavourable for them to do aught but defy their foes.

Mardonius asks Artabazus and the other generals for their advice. Artabazus, who also sees what Mardonius sees and who feels what he feels, says:

"Let us gather reinforcements in Thrace. There we will find support, supplies and food. Listen to me, Mardonius! Let us, if possible, end this war without further fighting. The entrails continue to predict misfortune for us. Let us no longer defy the gods. They are against us. Send gold to the allied Greeks, bullion gold and coined gold, as well as silver, and all the numerous drinking vessels of precious metal which the king left behind for us! Send all these treasures to the Greeks! Send them to those among them who are in power!"

The Theban generals endorse Artabazus' counsel. They advise caution. The gods are not kindly disposed.

"The gods!" cries Mardonius and raises himself to his full height. Madly, as though seized by an ecstasy, he again cries: "Which gods? The Greek gods to whom we have sacrificed?"

"Our gods!" said Artabazus.

"I shall make further sacrifices," says Mardonius,

[272]

and his generals look at him with horror. "I shall honour the Persian law and fight according to the Persian rule. Too long have I put my faith in soothsayers born beneath these enemy skies. I no longer trust them. Our gods will aid us and my army is strong."

No one contradicts him. He is the captain-general. He always had wanted this war and now, in spite of everyone and everything, he wants a battle.

They see him stand before them, panting. He is a tragic figure, like some hero of the tragedies to come. He looks around and says challengingly:

"Does any man among you know of an oracle which predicts to the Persians that I shall die in Hellas?"

All are silent. Some turn away their heads.

Mardonius cries:

"Since you either do not know or do not dare say, I myself shall tell you what I know to be the truth. An oracle predicted our defeat in case we looted the temple of Delphi. Our gods prevented us from despoiling the Delphian temple by means of an earthquake. Nor will we ever loot that shrine. We will respect the will of the gods, and be grateful to them for their protection. We shall defeat the Greeks."

He motions for them to go. Gloomily the generals leave the tent.

"There is the oracle of Bacis!" said one of the Thebans, outside.

"What does it say?" asks Artabazus.

The Theban glances around him. All crowd about to listen. He whispers:

"Gaze at the host of the Hellenes and hark to the medley of tongues

Of all the aliens on the edge of the reedy bed of
Æsopus!
Countless numbers of Medes will sink earthward
of Medes who use bows when fighting,
More than the Parcæ decreed, when destiny's
hour draweth nearer."

"There are many oracles of similar import," says
a Thessalian.

The Thessalian begins to whisper. Artabazus
turns away. He wishes to hear no more. Even
without oracles he knows what Fate will bring. He
had seen and he has sensed it.

## CHAPTER LII

## ALEXANDER'S WARNING

NIGHT descended. A dark, starless quiet spread over the plain, over the hills, over the river, over both camps, here the Persians, yonder the Greeks. The sentinels were at their posts. With their exception all seemed to sleep. The riddle of the coming day was hidden in sleep and silence and darkness. It was one of those moments of strange serenity which so often precede the thundering tempest of destiny, and the sentinels, almost alarmed by the exceeding quiet, were on the alert.

The Greek sentinels, watching and listening, saw a horseman ride quietly across the plain from the

Persian camp toward the Greek. Man and horse stood out as a dark silhouette against the grey night. When he drew near he answered the sentinel's challenge by saying he wished to speak to the Athenian leader. His tone was one of command, and two of the guard went off to report to the general that a horseman had come from the Persian camp.

The captains came to the outer edge of guard-posts through the darkness. The horseman in the black mantle did not move.

"What do you wish?" they asked him.

He led his horse two paces nearer, then replied:

"I have come, Athenians, to disclose a secret. I beg all of you to acquaint Pausanias with it, in case he is not among you. In the dark I cannot tell whether he is. I am a Greek. My race harks back to the grey dawn of Hellas. I do not wish to see Hellas bow beneath the Persian yoke. So I am come to tell you that the entrails remain unfavourable to Mardonius. Had they shown themselves favourable a battle would have been fought long ago. Yet, nevertheless, Mardonius is determined to attack."

"When?"

"Tomorrow. He fears that your army is growing. Prepare yourselves! If you defer the battle then do not leave your position. He has only two days' supplies."

"Why do you betray those in whose ranks you fight?"

The horseman did not reply. He continued:

"When this war has ended according to your wishes, then be just to him who, out of love for Hellas, dared the utmost to let you know Mardonius' plans!"

"Who are you?"

"Do you not know my voice? I am Alexander, son of Amyntas. I am Alexander of Macedon, who carried a message to you in Athens."

Slowly he turned his horse. His dark silhouette vanished in the night, gloomily, sorrowfully, like uncertainty's self, in the direction of the Persian camp.

The captains woke Pausanias in his tent. He feared the Persians and said:

"Athenians! You lie opposite the Bœotians. It would be better if you made a change and gathered opposite the Persians, whose mode of warfare is familiar to you from Marathon. We Spartans have never yet fought against them, but we know those traitors, the Bœotians and Thessalians. Let us exchange places. Do you take the right! We will take the left!"

"We had come to make you the same proposal," said the Athenian captains.

That day the Athenians and Spartans changed places. The Bœotians reported it to Mardonius, and Mardonius at once ordered the Persians to change places with the Bœotians, so that again they confronted the Spartans. Pausanias, when he was apprised of this, ordered the Athenians to change their position anew.

A Persian herald appeared on the plain. He blinked his eyes at the rising sun.

Mockingly he cried:

"Lacedæmonians! You are called the bravest of your land, and boast that you never have fled nor do you leave your post during battle, but deal out death or receive it wherever you may stand."

He laughed with scorn and added:

"Yet nothing is less true. Already you flee without fighting. You resign to the Athenians the honour of measuring themselves with us. You give our slaves, slaves of your own blood, the preference, the more safely to endure the battle. Bitterly you disappoint us. We had thought you would send us a herald, to challenge us, the Persians. Yet you tremble with fear and have already twice changed places this morning. So now *we* challenge *you*. Why should we not fight, since we are equal in number, you, the bravest—ha, ha, ha!—among the Greeks, and we, who in your eyes are only cowardly Barbarians? Let the outcome of the battle be decided by us alone. After us fresh troops, if need be, can carry on the fight! Yet I think it will be enough if you Spartans and we Persians settle among ourselves which is to be considered the victor."

The proud herald challengingly awaited his answer. He was one of those who had neither seen nor sensed. The voice of Persia's destiny was silent. The Greeks were silent. The Persian shrugged his shoulders, whistled contemptuously and trotted back, glancing around to dodge any chance arrow that might be sent after him. And contemptuously he continued to mouth insults from a distance. True, no sound could be heard, but the movements of his lips showed he was speaking of old women and contemptible cowards.

He reported that the Spartans were afraid to venture, that cowards, trembling with fear, they had made no reply. Mardonius now grew jubilant. He felt like embracing this haughty herald, this splendid, unapproachable hero. He ordered his horsemen to gallop over the plain and to provoke the Greeks with still greater insolence. Soon the plain was teeming with cavalry, the whole open plain between

Æsopus and Mount Cithæron swarmed with the magnificent Persian Immortals. The shining horsemen sparkled and glittered. They cast the lance, drew bow and pointed arrow in masterly fashion, aureoled by the glory of strength gracefully exercised. The outlines of these mounted bowmen, completely besprinkled with gold, on their handsome, coal-black horses, stood out at the beginning of the battle against the sere and fallow plain in lines most distinctly drawn, and with an ever-irradiant sparkle of shield and helm. And their arrows, crisscrossing in thick clouds, whirred in every direction, arrows that never miss their mark, so their senders boasted.

### CHAPTER LIII

## PAUSANIAS

THE Greeks are not equal to the fantastic Persian cavalry. Their horsemen are now here, now there. Their archery seems sport to them. They seem to be carrying on a sham battle against the still somewhat hesitant Greeks, but their arrows strike down many a man. It is a torrid day, and the Persians prevent the Greeks from approaching the spring of Gargaphia. This is the spring at which the whole Greek army quenches its thirst. The Greeks are uneasy. They have no supplies. They suffer from hunger and thirst on this sultry day.

Pausanias holds council with the generals. Perhaps it might be better to occupy the so-called island, that lies close by Platæa, between the two branches of the river. That very night they will march there, says Pausanias, if only to escape this Persian cavalry which is driving them mad. Suddenly the Greeks feel and realize that there is an uncertainty in the sultry air, an uncertainty which drifts along the hills and across the plain, and that an uncertainty rules their souls as well. There is something uncertain about Pausanias. They see it. He shows it, they feel it in him. And yet he is of the same family as Leonidas, and their forebears are the same.

Determined to pass over to the island that night, they nevertheless remain exposed to the provocations of the Persian horse throughout the day. Against their will they admire these radiant horsemen. Yet during the night they manage to gain the water-girded island, and encamp there not far from the Heraion, Hera's temple, at Platæa.

The day of Platæa dawns, the sun of Platæa rises. When Mardonius was informed in the morning that the Greeks had changed their camping ground, he cried out jubilantly to the Thessalian generals:

"What have you to say now, now that the Greeks have left their camp? You claimed the Lacedæmonians would never flee, and that they were the bravest men in the world! Yet first they twice changed position in the battlefront and camp. And now they have finally taken to flight. They are cowards amid the other Greeks, who also are cowards. Yet I forgive you for praising them. You knew them only; you did not know the Persians. I was more surprised when even Artabazus, a Persian, seemed to fear the Lacedæmonians and wanted to let our army

[281]

fall back on Thebes. The king shall hear of that some day. For the present, however, we'll see to it that these fleeing Greeks do not escape. Let us follow and destroy them once and for all today!"

The whole Persian host crosses the Æsopus. It streams over the plain in a far-flung wave of footmen and horsemen. With cheers and view-halloos it trots on in immeasurable breadth, to meet the sun of Platæa, convinced that the Greeks have actually fled, and that they must follow the trail of their march toward the island. The Athenians, established in the foothills of Mount Cithæron, do not at first see the Persians. As soon as they behold them stream shouting across the plain, the Athenians pluck their standards out of the ground, and run across the hills and levels with terrible roars and outcrys.

A herald, whom Pausanias in his obsessing hesitancy has dispatched to the Athenians, comes trotting across the hills to meet them. He shouts that the whole Persian cavalry is charging the Lacedæmonians. He calls on the Athenians for aid. He begs them at least to send some archers. For on foot they cannot withstand the shock of the Persian horse. The whole Athenian army, howling and roaring, sweeps down the hill and across the plain in the wake of the Persians, who do not expect them in their rear. They are heavily-armed hoplites. The Persian bowmen fling round their rearing, neighing horses in surprise, half-turn in their saddles, and bring their arrows to bear on them. A cloud of arrows darkens the air. The arrows intercross, as though, suddenly flaming up, they were spinning a dark net, immediately reft asunder, across the horizon. The irresistible arrows, the myriads of arrows make it impossible for the Athenians to draw nearer.

## CHAPTER LIV

## ON PLATÆA'S PLAIN

THE Spartans are sacrificing on the island, and
the soothsayers are reading the entrails. They
are sacrificing while the pick of their soldiers,
fifty thousand men, are facing the Persians. But the
entrails remain unfavourable to the Spartans, and
meanwhile the Persian horsemen are shooting from
behind a wall of shields—one man's shield close
beside the next man's, the other's close above him—
they are shooting thousands of arrows over the heads
of the Persian footmen, who are shooting other thousands in front of them. A darkness of arrows weighs
the terrible, sultry, heavily hanging and fateful light

of this strange late summer sun, which shines without a gleam of gold in a sky that is cloudless and yet not blue. Yonder fall hundreds of Spartans, stricken by the inescapable darts. There, in the middle of the island, Pausanias raises his eyes and hands to Hera's temple and in a loud voice prays to the goddess for aid.

No sooner has he made his fervent prayer than the entrails of a freshly slaughtered victim show—A miracle!—signs favourable to the Greeks. Can it be true? Pausanias' uncertainty has suddenly disappeared. No sooner are they aware that the gods are well inclined than the hesitation of the fifty thousand Spartans is gone. It seems as though there had been a revelation in the souls of the erstwhile hesitant warriors. In a furious onset the Lacedæmonians, in closely serried ranks, scorning the clouds of arrows, fling themselves on the Persians. The Median arrows strike beyond the Spartans' impetuous charge. Lacedæmonians and Persians are very close to one another, separated only by a wall of shields. The Persians fall back upon the Demetreion, the temple of Demeter, which, with its ancient walls and heavy expanse of gables, towers monstrously and fraught with destiny, as though to oppose the Persians' flight. The bursting wall of Persian shields splits, showing broad gaps. Persians and Greeks are fighting hand to hand. The Persians stoop and wrest the spears from the fists of the Greeks. And they struggle in a battle-fury that flames equally high on either side, one against one, two against two, ten against ten, under the flailing hoofs of the wildly plunging horses. Yet the Persian footmen are but lightly armed. Heavily armed, on the other hand, are the Greek hoplites who press ever thunderingly nearer.

In the thickest of the mêlée Mardonius appears on his white steed, eyes rolling furiously, sword in hand. He leads his Immortals and spurs them on. The irony of their name! They fall by the dozen round about him, they fall because of their courage, inflamed to temerity, because of their rage, turning to utter rashness. And never for a moment does the possibility of defeat occur to them, as it never occurs to them that the long Median robe fluttering beneath their armour hinders them while fighting, nor that the delicate, gracile weapons they bear, together with bow and arrow, cannot withstand the heft of the heavy Greek arms. So long as they can see their general in their midst, their general who leads them and urges them on, they fight tooth and nail, and stretch great numbers of Lacedæmonians upon the field.

Yet suddenly they see with surprise that Mardonius is engaged in a furious duel with a Spartan. The Spartan Arimnestos has attacked him. The swords of both engage, thrust and parry, behind their shields. The Immortals press up in a crowd to free Mardonius. Then they see their general give a sudden, pain-distorted gesture, and sink back into his saddle. He raises a clenched fist to heaven, threatening the gods, the gods of Hellas! The sword falls from his hand.

A shout of rage bursts from the crowding masses of the Persians.

But Arimnestos calls out in a loud voice:

"This day the death of Leonidas is avenged on Mardonius!"

No sooner have the Immortals seen their general fall—it is possible that a moment long they think of

securing his body, which has slid from his horse
into the battle-press—than they turn in disorder,
howling loudly with rage and despair, and take to
flight. It seems as though all this enormous host,
which has come such a distance to punish the Greeks,
is in the twinkling of an eye unnerved and dissolved.
The Persians flee in crowds. It seems as though the
figure of Demeter herself, the goddess, before her
temple, prevents the fugitives from taking refuge in
her fane and in her sacred grove, where as petitioners
they would be practically inviolable. They flee
around the temple, they storm back into the plain.

"Let all follow me, whither I lead, as soon as I
give the word of command, so that we may march
the more speedily."

Thus Artabazus had spoken to the forty thousand
men he wished to save, even before this moment of
universal flight, when he saw that Mardonius was
attempting the impossible. He now orders them to
march at the double-quick. They think Artabazus
is leading them against the enemy by a detour. But
Artabazus knows that all is lost. He has seen it,
he has felt it, and to struggle against fate and against
the gods is neither necessary nor of any avail. He
flees. He flees with his troops. Not to the wooden
wall still protecting the camp, nor even to Thebes.
Making a broad detour, he flees to Phocis. He wants
to return to Thessaly, he wants to return to Persia,
no matter how far away, no matter how unattainable Susa may seem to be. He wants to get away,
to tell the king that to struggle against fate and
against the gods is neither necessary nor of any avail.

Everywhere across the plain, that fatal plain of
Platæa, the Persians are in flight. And with them
flee all the allies their gold has bought, though the

Thebans for a time hold their own against the Athenians. The thousands flee in swarms. Enwrapped in clouds of dust they flee toward the far horizon, toward the north, toward the northwest, in a rout that is an epic panic, in a tremendous rout, a rout of peoples once allied, yet now dispersed by Mardonius' death. Of what use to keep on fighting now that Mardonius is slain? They all flee, because the despairing Persians are the first to set the example of flight.

The Greeks pursue the fugitives. A final skirmish takes place. The Bœotian cavalry makes a brief stand. But it is a general, colossal flight, a flight that is one terrible, pitiless massacre. Many Persians and thousands of other fleeing Barbarians have crowded into the Persian camp behind the Æsopus, behind the wooden walls from which the wooden watch towers project at regular intervals. In all haste they throw up further entrenchments. For a time they even succeed in standing off the Lacedæmonians, unskilled in the capture of fortified places. But the Athenians come to the latter's aid; the wooden walls crash, and the Greeks storm the Persian camp. There, amid the others, rise the splendid tents of the generals. Yonder, somewhat higher still, shows the tip of Mardonius' purple tent. There the Persian slaves beg for mercy, there the women, wives and concubines of the Persian leaders tremblingly hide themselves, there the Greeks loot Mardonius' pavilion. They carry off his seat of state, with its silver feet, the extravagantly sumptuous gold and silver furniture, the precious table service. They laugh at the camels. They carry off the bronze mangers of Mardonius' chargers, marvels of Persian sculpture. All that is most beautiful among

[287]

the loot will be dedicated to the gods in their temples.

Of an army of three hundred thousand men, only three thousand unarmed slaves, begging for mercy, narrowly escape death.

Artabazus flees to Phocis, flees by long detours, with his forty thousand, in order to bring Xerxes the news.

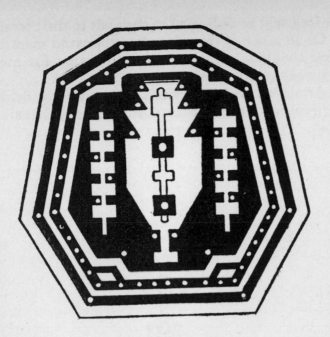

## CHAPTER LV

## THE BLACK SOUP OF SPARTA

"PILE up all the booty here!" ordered Pausanias. "See that not one of you, ye Greeks, take so much as a coin or a cup for his own!"

The helots, Sparta's slaves, drag the booty to one spot in the middle of the camp. They bring on the rolled-up tents, the tapestries and stuffs woven of gold and silver, the gold and silver couches, the gold and silver bowls and censers and drinking-cups. The plainest of kitchen utensils are of copper and bronze. They strip the countless dead of their chains and armlets of honour, and their choicely worked daggers, inlaid with rounded stones. Into the presence of the assembled generals they lead the Nisæan steeds, the mirth-provoking camels. The timorous train of innumerable women concludes the procession.

There are no needless, unmerciful cruelties. The coined money and the treasure in caskets and chests are counted, arranged and recorded. One tenth will be offered the gods. Of this fund the victors, later, will weld the golden tripod around which writhe three bronze serpents, and which stands on the heads of the three serpents, for the temple of Delphi. And for Olympia will be cast the bronze Zeus, ten cubits in height; and for the Isthmus the bronze Poseidon, seven cubits high. A second tenth is offered to Pausanias. It includes women, horses, camels, some talents of silver, all sorts of goods. Every one who has distinguished himself on the day of Platæa, so fateful to the Persians, receives his share of the astounding reward. What luxury, what extravagance! How many useless things had been dragged hither out of Persia! How many slaves and women, as though a Persian general's tent were the Persian court! Pausanias laughs, although all these costly objects which he examines with the other captains, and allows to glide through his fingers, nevertheless make a certain impression on him: a small chest filled with toilet accessories; a charger's gold-mounted bridle; an honorary armlet. He laughs, though in a manner somewhat forced, yet finds that all these things are very beautiful, and commands:

"Send hither all the cooks, cellarers and bakers of Mardonius!"

They present themselves in rank and file, their chief at their head.

"Prepare a meal for me this evening such as you would have set before your master!" he tells them.

[290]

The kitchen slaves get to work. The cellarers mingle bayberry honey with palm wine. The silken umbrellas are raised on their poles, the couches mounted in gold and silver are put in order. The most delicate dishes smoke upon the table.

Yet Pausanias at the same time has commanded that a meal be prepared in Lacedæmonian style.

In all its simplicity the black soup waits in the uncovered wooden bowls.

Laughing, Pausanias points out the difference to his officers.

"Hellenes!" he cries. "Now you may see the folly of the Persian king, and of his brothers, brothers-in-law and nephews. Having so excellent a table they nevertheless envied ours. We will not imitate them, but instead sit down to our own Spartan simplicity!"

He sat down to the black soup. And the rest followed his example, while across from them the Persian slaves—as well as the tricked-out slave-girls, who think the gentle-mannered victors will ask them to play and dance—stand staring with mouths wide-opened, because the Greeks do not even seem to care to touch this sumptuously prepared banquet.

Yet perhaps at that very moment there crept into the soul of Pausanias the Spartan a strange curiosity with regard to this Persian luxury which he now disdained. Perhaps at that very moment the god of luxury implanted in the simple soldier's soul the poisonous germ that some day was to lead him to drape himself in a Median robe, to eat after the Persian manner, and to sue for the hand of Xerxes' daughter, who would bring about his destruction.

Yet this was still the day of Platæa.

## CHAPTER LVI

## PERSIA'S HEAVY HOUR

THAT same evening was the evening of Mycale, on which the remainder of the Persian fleet was beaten by the sea forces of the allies in the Ionian Sea, and Nike flew from the opened hand of Zeus to meet the Greeks, there as here, at Platæa as at Mycale. The god of the Persians to whom Xerxes always appealed, had not aided Xerxes.

\* \* \*

The days drag on in Susa. They are once more the sultry oppressive days of summer. Thousands of roses are in profusest bloom. In the porticoes of the court the women are busy making sweet preserves and rose-pods are steeping in boiling sugar. It is true that the war still rages. It is true that fear and depression are rife, because the couriers Mardonius was to send do not come. It is true that no torches, with swift flame-signals in the night, announce a decisive victory, and the destruction of the rebellious Greeks at Athens, or wherever it may be in Attica, or perhaps even on the Isthmus. Yet at the same time this is the season of roses, and it would be a shame not to pluck them, it would be a shame not to preserve them, and not to candy the precious seed-pods. The royal widows, Atossa, Artystone, Parmys and Phaidyme sit as of old on their couches. Amestris has but just once more coaxed the tale of pseudo-Smerdis from Phaidyme, and all those eager to gain the queen's favour listen and giggle. Artaxixa is busy preserving and Artaynte, her daughter—the incident of the mantle and Xerxes' brief passion for her are long since things of the past —is attentively watching Artozostra. For the great loom now stands before Artozostra, the wife of Mardonius, and around her the slave-girls compete as to who shall wind the purple silk and threads of gold on the various spools. Artozostra is weaving a mantle for her husband Mardonius, to whose return in triumph from the war she looks forward. And Artaynte, now the wife of Darius, the youthful heir apparent,—still a mere boy, who does not live with her but in the camp of youths, where he is perfecting himself in knightly exercises,—Artaynte admires the mantle Artozostra is weaving for Mardonius. She whispers in her ear that this mantle will be far more beautiful than the one Amestris wrought for Xerxes, and which she, Artaynte, had owned for a few days.

And Artozostra, feeling flattered, and longing for Mardonius' return, warns her to lower her voice, lest Amestris hear her.

"I know a prophecy," one slave-girl winding purple silk thread whispers to another who is gathering skeins out of a basket, behind Artozostra's back.

"What is it?" asks the other, without interest. Prophecies are numberless at the Persian court, though they never even remotely hint at a possible defeat of Mardonius' army.

"That Prince Darius will not become the King of Kings, but will die young, and Artaxerxes wear the crown."

The slave-girl gathering skeins shrugged her shoulders indifferently. Yet suddenly both cast themselves to the ground, and all the other slave-girls followed their example. For the word "Sun" had been spoken. Artozostra, content with her work, has said to Artaynte:

"The Sun on the outside of the mantle will be beautiful."

"Holy!" murmur all the slave-girls who had cast themselves down on the marble tiles.

From without sounds a noise that grows in volume. Can it be—at last—the smoothly working Persian royal post, bringing letters from Mardonius and all the princes who had remained with him, letters to mothers, wives and daughters?

"It must be the royal mail," says Queen Amestris. "It is a long time since I have heard anything from my father Otanes."

It is not the royal mail. Yet what it is cannot at once be determined. It is an indefinite noise that swells, swells through the inner courtyard from the wing of the palace where Xerxes' apartments are situated. The women are much alarmed. They do not know what it may be. They think of murder, arson, all sorts of terrible catastrophes. The thought of a disaster never occurs to them, for at all times they have had only tidings of victory from Hellas. Athens was twice taken. They knew nothing of Thermopylæ. And Xerxes had disposed of Salamis in two words. It was true that their brothers, sons and nephews had fallen there. Yet they had mourned and wept them, and had counted upon the victorious Persians avenging all those who had fallen victims to the war. So the possibility of bad news from Hellas still does not occur to them, though they think of murder, fire and even more terrible catastrophes. All rush up, trembling with curiosity: the dowager queens, Amestris, the young princesses, all the concubines, all the slaves. They rush from the inner court to the apartments of the king. There stand the guards, the eunuchs, the court officials. Indescribable confusion reigns until, suddenly, in his reception hall, which is open, they see Xerxes, his eyes bewildered, his hands clenched, and, in front of him Artabazus, who, so they thought, was in Hellas, or Europe, as they were wont to say. They heard Xerxes ask:

"And Mardonius?"

"Mardonius has fallen," replied Artabazus.

One tremendous cry rose from the lips of the women. Their arms are flung heavenward in a single tremendous gesture of despair, and Artozostra screams:

"Mardonius! Mardonius has fallen!"

She cannot believe it. It is incredible. She and Artystone, Mardonius' grandmother, cast themselves into each other's arms. Atossa removes the curious

[295]

slave-girls in her path with a light blow of her whip. She approaches her son. Young Prince Darius, Artaynte's husband, has hurried up from the camp of the youths. Even Artaxerxes, still a child, has come running up with his tutor and his eunuchs from the interior of the palace.

Artabazus repeats:

"Mardonius has fallen."

Again the cry, again the gesture. Despair floods the palace like a tidal wave. The very least slave now knows that Mardonius has fallen. All hasten up, irresistibly. They want to hear Artabazus tell how the fateful battle of Platæa was fought and how Mardonius fell.

"Coward! You fled!" cried Xerxes.

Artabazus admits it. He fled, fled with forty thousand men. It was no longer possible to fight, he avers. Since the king reproaches him with his flight he regrets that he has not fought, that he has not fallen. But he did not flee because of cowardice. He fled because he had *seen* and *felt,* because it was no longer possible to keep on fighting and he wished to repeat this to the king.

"Who else would have brought the tidings to Susa?" Artabazus cries. "What does life mean to me after the shame that has been poured out upon the head of every Persian!"

"Where is your army?" cried Xerxes.

"Where is my army? I managed to lead it to Thessaly. I told the Thessalians, who as yet knew nothing of Platæa, that Mardonius with his hosts was following on our heels. I told them I had to push on. I fled on. The Thessalians believed me. Had they not, they would have revolted and would have slain me, O King! No one would have brought the news to Susa. But thus, thus I could flee, and I fled through Thrace. The river beds were dry, there was no trace of grain in the fields. Everywhere I lost men. They fell along the roads. The plague or the Thracians made away with them. The whole road from Thessaly to Byzantium is sown with the corpses of my soldiers, and the carrion birds are feasting on them."

The wailing, the long drawn-out lamentations of the women, the thousands of women who had all turned into weeping mourners, the thousandfold gesture of arms outstretched to heaven fills the courtyard, the porticoes, the whole palace. It enwraps the grandmother and wife of Mardonius, and his young children, who have come running up, with a clamorous blanket of despair. And this despair pours through the palace, it streams into the city, and suddenly everyone in Susa knows about it. Everyone knows about Thermopylæ, knows about Salamis, knows about Platæa. Everyone, everyone knows that the god of the Persians has not helped his people. Everyone knows that the Persian armies have been beaten, the Persian fleets destroyed, armies in their millions, counting the allied nations over whom the king rules, fleets of thousands of vessels— all have been beaten and destroyed, though the sea was whipped, the mountain pierced, though world dominion had once been granted Persia, in the days when Cyrus lived.

Xerxes has fled into his chamber before that cry of despair. He has cast himself on his couch and stares through the open windows into the gardens. Unmoved, the palm-trees raise their crowns of feathery leaves toward the summer blue of the sky. Everything seems untouched: the torsos of the bulls that support the cedarwood beams, the pacing lions of glazed tile that cover the walls and, in relief, the monstrous, spear-bearing, tremendously muscular warriors in enamel by the door. Xerxes stares before him and asks himself how it can be possible. His brothers Abrocomes and Hyperanthes at Thermopylæ, his brother Ariabignes and his nephews and brothers-in-law at Salamis, Tigranes—how tall and splendid he was—and Mardonius at Platæa and Mycale, Artayntes, Ithametres, all dead! Woe, woe! All dead!

It drives him mad, he cannot credit it. A few boorish Dorians surely cannot threaten the whole Persian civilization! He rises, walks up and down, he listens. He feels as though the women's shrill, uncontrolled cries of sorrow and despair pierce not only his ears but his brain. He sinks back on his cushions, he crashes down in his crushed arrogance and stares, stares before him as though mad.

Framed in the unclosed door, in front of a half-drawn curtain in the entrance between the giant spearmen of enamel and glazed stone, human figures are visible. They are six officers of the royal body-guard. Their commander—Artabanus is his name —leads them. Their swords are drawn, they have regicide in mind. They have been dissatisfied with the war. Artabanus, son of Artabanus, Xerxes' nephew, himself is eager to wear the Persian crown. Seven together, they will murder Xerxes as Darius and the six Persians once murdered pseudo-Smerdis. Artabanus will murder Xerxes, the boy Darius, the boy Artaxerxes. Is this not the moment, the moment that must be improved, the moment to commit the murder? And then to keep it secret while the corpse is laid on the *dakhma*, the "Tower of

Silence," for the vultures, and then to stir up hatred
in the city against the king who lost the war with
Hellas, who let his army be beaten and his fleet
destroyed. And after that they would prepare the
rising in the palace. Behold! Yonder lies Xerxes,
crumpled together with his arrogance, there he lies,
staring before him like a madman. Is this not the
moment?

For some minutes the ambitious conspirators hesitate. They consider, they vacillate.

But the grief of the women rings in their ears, and
it unnerves the covetous daring of the men.

"No, no!" whispers Artabanus, son of Artabanus,
"later, later."

The officers retire. Artabanus retires. The curtain falls into place. Nothing moves: the gigantic
mosaics, the lions on the frieze, the palms in the garden, and Xerxes, staring before him like a madman.

"Mardonius!" he moans plaintively, "Mardonius!
Ithamethres! Ariabignes! Abrocomes! Hyperanthes!"

"Mardonius!" the wail of sorrow echoes from
far, far away in the harem apartments, and is re-
echoed now here, now there:

"Mardonius!"

## CHAPTER LVII

## SEVEN YEARS LATER

IT WAS seven years later. In these years following the famous victory Athens had become a new city, the first in Hellas. Athens had flowered into a city more blooming than all others of Hellas, fairer in blossom than Sparta, Megara or Sicyon, a city already forecasting the miracle that was to take place some decades later. The golden age was germinant with budding splendour. It already showed its opening buds in Athens, which had been rebuilt with feverish eagerness, and was full of an ardent vitality seeking to blaze new trails in every direction. Athens was full of an intoxicating vital power, which was to inspire all its youthful activities with a glorious new impulse. It was to revivify her daring commercial ventures, rivalling those of Phœnicia, the genial diplomacy of the young seapower, already famous, her even more genial intellectual development. And this last it was to raise up to the utmost limit human wisdom ever has attained. It was to develop it into the most gifted artistry of word, line and form—poetry, sculpture and architecture—in an apotheosis of human ability in its supremest perfection.

It was seven years after Platæa. The great festivals of the Athenian Dionysus were in progress, festivals instituted by Peisistratus, yet which, after the Persian war, were celebrated every year with enhanced spirit and nobler splendour in honour of the naval hegemony which Athens had won over all the other Hellenic states. They were the three holy days dedicated to the god Dionysus, as he was understood in Athens—a god of life and youth, of joy and jubilation. And Dionysus was understood in Athens as, perhaps, nowhere else in Greece. It was the ninth day of the month Elaphebolion, which corresponds to the month of April in the chronology of later centuries. Its sunlight was the sunlight of the south, the intoxicating sunlight of Attica, blond as the honey of Hymettus.

And with the hum of bees in the far, deep, transparent air was mingled the hum of the multitude that overflowed the streets and squares, the Agora and the slopes of the Areopagus, near the Acropolis. There it swarmed about the old temple of Pallas Athene, soon to become the miraculous shrine of the Parthenon and which, still standing, awaiting its metamorphosis, or descended to the theatre of Dionysus, the theatre dedicated to the god of these joyous days.

The violets, the violets of Attica, wound in wreaths, and roses, the flowers of blossoming beauty, gathered in nosegays, were bought by every man and woman in the throng who felt within the irresistible intoxication, not of the Dionysian grape—whose purple ripeness would glow only after this season when the pulse beat high—but the intoxication of the jubilant Dionysian joy in life and the power of happiness. During these days it irradiated air and light, tremulous, quivering, as though throughout the ether there were suspended invisible lyres, vibrant with music.

All the friends of Athens, all her allies, had come in festival attire over the roads white with dust, or across the water, and on this morning the theatre of Dionysus, in front of which all the crowds merged in one sea of humanity, was opened. For the mood of gladness and inspired enjoyment of life was mingled and intimately interwoven with an æsthetic mood of deep yearning for art. The delight of the Dionysia merged in a lofty transition of gentle harmony with desire for the enjoyment of ultimate beauty, even tragic beauty. For to witness and to share the experience of a tragedy, if indeed it be an elevated work of art, need not depress one nor estrange one from the joy of happy living.

This morning was the first day of the dramatic contest. Three poets were to compete for the prize awarded the best tragedy on that day. Clever, comic-satiric plays would precede the performance of their three tragedies, which would be given one after the other. And satiric comedy was welcomed by this gaiety-loving people, witty in conversation, quick in estimate and not sentimental.

There was no rain to be apprehended during these days. The sun promised an agreeable sitting, since at this season it shone without a torrid glow. There was room for thousands and thousands. Stone benches had been set up for the Archons and other officials in front of the orchestra, before the round platform of great stone slabs. In the middle of this platform rose the *thymele,* the plain altar of Dionysus, on whose steps the flute-player, who regulated the step of the marching chorus or accompanied its dances with his modulations, seated himself.

The theatre was not as yet an architectural monument, and the beauty of the whole rested solely on the crowded, hydra-headed assembly of spectators whom the Dionysia had put in a happy frame of mind, and who had come from far and wide, over land and sea. Beauty still rested exclusively in the unpretentious, spontaneous interest taken by the spectators in the tragic poems which the three competing poets would present that day, after the satiric comedies.

Long and lasting was the treat. Yet great was the patience and the devotion of the people. It might, indeed, still appreciate the primordial unconstraint of comedy, but for it tragedy possessed a greater, a highly solemn, religious significance. This feeling was still as strong a century before, in Solon's day, when Thespis strolled about with his cart, on which the Dionysiac mysteries were represented, and when he, as the sole actor, personified the three rôles of the tragedy in a costume that was no more than a drapery of grape-leaves.

With entire psychic absorption this audience composed of Athenians and their allies followed the works of the poets, their merry political satires, and then their usually mythic tragedies, in which men were arrogant and guilty, the gods often pitiless, yet just; and in which Fate was the omnipotent arbiter. Yet when the last drama by the last of the three poets was to be enacted, tremendous excitement swept the entire crowd sitting crammed on the wooden benches or penned on the grassplots.

The name of the poet—he was now no longer an unknown—passed from mouth to mouth in respectful whispers. Æschylus, son of Euphorion. He had fought at Marathon, at Salamis, at Platæa. He had already exhibited in competition with Pratinas and had often gained the prize. This new drama the poet called *The Persians*. Into it he had introduced a second actor. To the protagonist he added the deuteragonist, "the answerer." The various rôles—in this new tragedy, *The Persians*, there were five such, including the choragus—were on this occasion divided between the two actors. And it was rumoured that during the interlude Æschylus himself would personify the protagonist. That was not surprising, since the poet often assumed the leading rôle.

A sacred curiosity held the audience—composed of beings who had absolutely abandoned themselves to the work—spellbound with intensity. Until it began they stared longingly at the still empty orchestra, at the still empty proscenium, behind which rose the *scena*, in the ancient theatre the edifice bounding the stage. Their panting, controlled with difficulty, was audible, their eyes were fixed, and their souls stared out from their eyes. A holy silence hung about this art which was to be revealed, and which was naught else but divine worship and beauty in one, to be resolved in the end into horror, emotion and conciliating pity. On the altar step the flute-player began his prelude.

Side-scenes were moved behind the proscenium to represent, in simple stylized lines, the entrances to a Persian palace. It was not the splendour of the hundreds of taurine columns, and the greenish-blue mosaic friezes with their marching lions, white and gold, that shone in Xerxes' palace. One could hardly call it Persian. The idea of a royal dwelling was outlined by no more than the simplest generalization. Before the plain row of columns there rose an equally simple mortuary pillar, meant to represent the grave of Darius, Xerxes' father. In reality the grave of Darius was represented by a profusion of columns, a colour-glowing relief of glorification above a rock before the gates of Susa. Here, in the theatre of Athens, it became no more than a faint hint. Yet it seemed to suffice.

Now, on either side, out of the palace portals, stepped six Elders, who descended the steps to the orchestra and walked past the flute-player. These twelve faithful servants of Xerxes, eminent among the Persians, formed the chorus, and their leader, the second actor, began to speak, and to say that they, guardians of this proud palace of the Persian kings, were beset by sinister presentiments.

Around the leader the chorus, together with him, expressed his excitement and his fears by gestures. The twelve Elders, wearing their head-masks with broad, funnel-shaped mouths, walked with long steps in their high-heeled buskins, in their long

[305]

Median robes—plainer than any worn by the least of Xerxes' servants—and, with the spacious movements of their artificially extended arms, appeared to be giants. Seen from the distance, from the farthest rungs of the circle and the highest steps of turf, they made a profoundly strange and intimidating impression that sunny morning, so that women screamed and clung trembling to their husbands, and children began to cry. A hissing that insisted on quiet, however, stilled the noise. The children were led away. The timid women sat silent, and the poet's words, given reverent attention, exercised their sway over the unstrung multitude. Ha! This was Persia, these were the Persian Elders, and they divined that fate which was to come. The twelve Elders spoke the sonorous names of the Persian and oriental kings who were tributaries of the supreme Basileus. They praised the princes and the kings, they praised the incomparable archers, the incomparable knights who followed them, and they lauded them in Greek, using the words of a Greek poet. No satire lurked in the lofty, sustained verses, though in the preceding comedy satirical allusions to the most recent happenings in Athens, and to prominent personalities might have occurred. At the very beginning of this tragedy there trembled in the poet's verses a pitying sense of dread that was in harmony with the feelings of these Persian grandees, who sensed with gloomy foreboding what was to come:

From all Asia the people him followed
Sword in hand. They obeyed
The stern command of their king.
The flower of Persia's manhood,

Its best are gone.
And with sorrowful longing
All Asia, that nursed them, mourns them,
And their parents and wives tremble for them.
Anxiously they count the dragging days.

There is no ironic inflection in these words of the Greek warrior-poet who thus presents his defeated opponents on the stage. All that it voices is the loftiest, noblest respect for the vanquished. Not even the quiet, secret joy of victory echoes in them. Only participation in the approaching sorrow of Persia. The spectators, all Greeks or allies, the warriors who seven years before had fought against these Persians to defend their homeland, are touched, for they are aware that this is holiest art, an art sprung from loftiest humanity.

While the poisonous basilisk's threatening glance
    lights his eyes—
Countless arms of warriors and countless speedy
    ships
He calls his, himself in a Syrian car driving fu-
    riously—
He sets on the Greeks, skilled in wielding the spear,
Persia's war-god, who knows but the bow.
Who so battle-tried that he can brave the strong
    onset
Of the sea-driven billow? Unconquerable is the
    sea's tide.
To be stemmed by no dam, though it be the most
    powerful sea-wall.
Yet the bravest warriors of Persia and our people's
    high spirit
None as yet have withstood.

The spectators, in spirit, once more see their dear natal land overrun by the Persian tidal wave.

Our king's city-destroying myriads of troopers
Have crossed to the land
Beckoning us as a neighbour.
Hempen cables raised their weak bridges
O'er the waters of Hellas.
Firmly-joined paths of wood laid
Themselves yokewise upon ocean's neck.

Full of courage, they learned to look boldly
On the sacred, illimitable flood of the ocean,
When furiously tossing, the hurricane
Whipped high the white-crested billows,
And, audacious, themselves confided
To thin-stranded cables and
Planks all asway to cross over.

The spectators shudder with pity, pity makes the
fighters of Marathon, of Salamis and Platæa tremble,
tremble with commiseration for those they had vanquished. Then the choregus says:

Yet behold!   Like the light in a god's eye
Draweth near our dread master's mother,
My queen.   Now kneel with me!
And with reverent word of greeting
Let her Highness approach us!
Ruler supreme of the noblest women in Persia's
   empire,
Worthy mother of Xerxes, Hail! wife of Darius!
You are the spouse of our god, mother of the god
   of the Persians,
If Fate's wonted treachery have not erst to the
   army proved fatal.

The crowded mass rises and stares.   This horror
which is approaching wakes in it a vibrant compassion, and its beauty makes them shudder.   For

Atossa, the mother, has stepped out of the palace. Her part is taken by the protagonist, and it is whispered that he is Æschylus, the poet himself. He wears the tragic female mask, he is shrouded in the broad, gold-embroidered purple mantle worn by queens, and as a result Atossa's figure seems monstrous and supernatural. Neither his movements nor his deep voice hold more than a suggestion of a natural female impersonation. This colossal figure, slowly moving forward with long steps, is terror-inspiring rather than feminine.

While Atossa declares her fear, and her touching verses sound out over the roofless theatre and above the heads of the Greeks who sit close-crowded therein, no Persian courtier in Susa would for a moment have associated the poet's creation with the spare, tyrannical, short-sighted old woman who, wrapped in violet veils, excitedly swings her whip in a hand that age has made uncertain. Yet this figure of the poet's imagination is tremendously impressive moving on its buskins, with its broad, anxious gestures, with its deep, hollow voice of lamentation, in which sings the disquiet of a divinely great mother's soul. It is loftier than any other impersonation could be on this day, in this hour of reverential sharing of emotion. The account of the dream that announces her fate, and that she communicates to the Elders, seems to come like a swelling breath of poesy from far, far haunts of the unknown and unseen, bearing with it on its oscillant rhythms the revelation of the inevitable.

In verses filled with fear the mother of Xerxes questions. In verses which already allow the misfortune to be divined, the spokesman of the Elders replies, until the messenger draws near, the second

[309]

actor, who confirms with moving outcries that what the Elders had dreaded, and what the mother had dreamed, has become truth at Salamis. The messenger comes from Salamis, and the spectators, violently excited, remember Salamis, where, seven years before, the Athenian fleet carried off the victory over the Asiatic ships in their thousands. It was unavoidable that, despite their divine compassion, human pride should rise up within them. Yet no rough outcry came from the crowd, not a single pitiless word of the poet's witnesses to a coarse, braggart triumph. The tragic Muse is still noble in her sympathy, as when she inspired the poet-actor while he wrote, as she inspires him now, while he acts. The mother, Atossa, begs the messenger to tell the tale of the battle of Salamis. Brimming over with recollections the spectators tremble, side by side, their eyes staring, and then their souls staring with their eyes.

How these ringing verses shimmer through the account of Persia's catastrophe like a glory through a cloud! How they irradiate the glory of Athens, the victory of Hellas, in their measured beauty! How their own joy in the emotional participation of their companions rises and sinks as on the waves of a universal sea of humanity!

Before the fixed eyes and souls of these spectators every thought of the stage, of performance and competition has disappeared. They experience only the noblest sympathy and most sacred joy that they have saved their fatherland for this day of purest triumph. Their tears flow because of the guilt of this king whose mother screams with anguish for him, yet their panting mouths smile because of their own joy, the joy the just gods have granted them. Their tension is well-nigh unbearable, because of all these overpowering recollections that have been roused in them.

And then the shade of Darius, summoned from the mortuary vault by the lamentations of the Persians, prophesies to Atossa and the Elders still more terrible catastrophes than that of Salamis, when it foretells what will occur after Salamis, what—as the spectators already know—did occur seven holy years ago, Darius' shade prophesies the events of Platæa. This account given by the shade of Xerxes' father is like a thundering proclamation of Fate.

And then the king himself appears, and the spectators forget that the gigantic figure which storms up in despair with torn mantle and empty quiver, is once again Æschylus, the poet himself who as protagonist is enacting both leading rôles. The spectators, in this despairing apparition, behold none other than Xerxes' own self, guilt chastised, arrogance annihilated. The emotion vicariously felt for him is scarce bearable, and no word of abuse is cast in his face. Only chests and bosoms rise and fall with the despairing rise and fall of the lines, mouths twitch, tears flow in silence, tears awakened in the souls of the victors for the sake of the vanquished by holy art. Xerxes clamours his despair, the twelve Elders, his echo, answer him:

"Persia's power is broken! Let us sorrow together! Beat your breasts, ye Elders! Tear your faces! Let the sorrowful, melancholy Mysian threnody sound! Tear your hair and beard! Weep for our lost hosts!"

Again and again the lament of the chorus rings

out sadly through space, rising toward the blue, motionless sky.

"Woe! Woe! And must we then let Persia witness our grief?"

Whereupon Xerxes, as though tearing at his own heart-strings cries:

"Yes, Persia shall bear witness, shall bear witness to our grief!"

The wild voices rise to a veritable ocean of overpoweringly tragic sound, which fills the entire auditorium.

"Alas for my ships! Alas for my hosts!"

"Woe! Woe! And must we then let Persia witness our grief?"

The performance suddenly comes to an end. The excitement roused by joy and sympathy has tensed the souls of the Greeks to the breaking-point. It was the loftiest emotion that art had ever been able to bestow on an Athenian audience. It is like an intoxication Dionysiac and Apolline in one. It is so overwhelming that the spectators almost forget to rejoice. Cries are heard here, there, everywhere, for the Archons, the city officials. The huge spreading expanse of the theatre seems all too small. This multitude feels as though it will suffocate in this semicircle beneath the blue, immovable sky.

All crowd out. They sense the need to give unconstrained expression to their feelings, and as though by an impulse in common they do not disperse, but climb the hill to the Areopagus. A young man, hardly more than a boy, beautiful as the statues of the sculptors to come, leads a group of youthful comrades. Seven years ago, not yet able to bear arms, their adolescent hearts had beaten violently in their breasts at the news of Salamis and Platæa. They had been disappointed because they could not share in the fighting. Now they were men, young men, and the past would have to do without them.

Yet they will inherit the future. Pericles, the youth who now leads his comrades and climbs the hill with them, will inherit the future. Their shouts thunder out on the spring air. The crowd follows their young enthusiasm. Where? To the Acropolis, to the ancient fane of Pallas Athene. Does Pericles see rise, behind that ancient sanctuary, like a radiant vision of the temple of the future, the vaguely luminous apparition of that Parthenon some day to be built? Yet their impatience has carried them to the old temple. They point it out to one another, and in their enthusiasm they utter joyous shouts, together with the names of the gods, the names Salamis and Platæa.

See! Yonder, between the Dorian columns which ring the *cella,* hang thousands of golden Persian shields that were the booty of Platæa. They hang from the columns, they lie high-piled above each other. They seem a thousand captured suns, suns which had crashed down in their superfluity from the heaven of humbled arrogance, and Pericles and his comrades lay hand on their daggers. Where daggers are lacking they clench their young fists, while the exalted crowd hurries up, eddies about them, to see, to know, to share the surging uplift of their divine intoxication. With the hilts of their daggers, with their clenched fists, veritable corybantes, they beat the thousands of shields till they rattle and ring, the heaped-up Persian shields, the conquered golden Persian suns of arrogance, till a monstrous clangour

[313]

sends its echoes flying the length of the Acropolis. And with the full, clear sonority of their strong, youthful voices, full of gladness and sacred emotion, they cry:

"Hellas!  Holy motherland!  Holy, holy motherland!"

COLLEGE LIBRARY
ST. JOSEPH'S COLLEGE
1852
Phila., Pa.